*To my wife and children*

THIS BOOK IS IN THE

**ADDISON-WESLEY SERIES IN INTRODUCTORY MATHEMATICS**

*Consulting Editors*

RICHARD S. PIETERS AND GAIL S. YOUNG

# AN INTRODUCTION TO
# ABSTRACT
# MATHEMATICAL
# SYSTEMS

**DAVID M. BURTON** | *University of New Hampshire*

 **ADDISON-WESLEY,** READING, MASSACHUSETTS

**ADDISON-WESLEY PUBLISHING COMPANY, INC.**

READING, MASSACHUSETTS  ·  Palo Alto  ·  London

NEW YORK  ·  DALLAS  ·  ATLANTA  ·  BARRINGTON, ILLINOIS

# PREFACE

This little volume is an outgrowth of a series of lectures given by the author in a summer institute for high school teachers of mathematics. The purpose of the course was to improve the participants' understanding of algebraic structure and to acquaint them with some of the basic results of abstract algebra through a formal investigation of various mathematical systems.

In putting these lectures into textbook form, our aim has been to give a presentation which is logically developed, precise, and in keeping with the spirit of the times. Thus a constant level of rigor has been maintained throughout with proofs given in full detail, except for those which parallel proofs given previously. The reader will also find that the text is essentially self-contained. A first chapter on sets and functions is being included to serve as background and to introduce some of the terminology and notations used subsequently. Numerous exercises of varying degree of difficulty are to be found at the end of each section.

It is hoped that the material encountered here will be adaptable to a variety of teaching situations and prove useful not only to the mathematics major but to any adequately prepared student. Indeed, to some extent this has already been the case, for certain mimeographed portions of this text have been successfully employed in a terminal course for liberal arts freshmen. The entire volume would be quite appropriate for a beginning one-semester course in modern algebra or for a reading course in which the student could master the material through independent study.

Many important topics vie for inclusion in a volume of this size, and some choice is obviously imperative. To this end, we merely followed our own taste, condensing or omitting altogether certain of the concepts found in the usual first course in modern algebra. Despite these omissions there remains a broad foundation upon which the reader can build.

*New Haven, Conn.*                                                                    D. M. B.
*April 1965*

# CONTENTS

*Chapter 1*

# PRELIMINARY NOTIONS

## 1-1. THE ALGEBRA OF SETS

The present chapter establishes some of the notations and terminology used throughout the text. It also serves as a brief introduction to the algebras of sets and functions. Inasmuch as this material is intended primarily for background purposes, the reader may prefer to begin with Chapter 2.

The term "set" is intuitively understood to mean a collection of objects having some common characteristic. The objects that make up a given set are called its *elements* or *members*. Sets will generally be designated by capital letters and their elements by small letters. In particular, we shall employ the following notations: $Z$ is the set of integers, $Q$ the set of rational numbers, and $R^{\#}$ the set of real numbers. The symbols $Z_+$, $Q_+$, and $R^{\#}_+$ will stand for the positive elements of these sets.

If $x$ is an element of the set $A$, it is customary to use the notation $x \in A$ and to read the symbol $\in$ as "belongs to." On the other hand, when $x$ fails to be an element of the set $A$, we denote this by writing $x \notin A$.

There are two common methods of specifying a particular set. First, we may list all of its elements within braces, as with the set $\{-1, 0, 1, 2\}$, or merely list some of its elements and use three dots to indicate the fact that certain elements have been omitted, as with the set $\{1, 2, 3, 4, \ldots\}$. When such a listing is not practical, we may instead indicate a character-istic property whereby we can determine whether or not a given object is an element of the set. More specifically, if $P(x)$ is a statement concerning $x$, then the set of all elements $x$ for which the statement $P(x)$ is true is denoted by

$$\{x \mid P(x)\}.$$

1

For example, we might have $\{x \mid x$ is an odd integer greater than 21$\}$. Clearly, certain sets may be described both ways:

$$\{0, 1\} = \{x \mid x \in Z \quad \text{and} \quad x^2 = x\}.$$

It is customary, however, to depart slightly from this notation and write $\{x \in A \mid P(x)\}$ instead of $\{x \mid x \in A \text{ and } P(x)\}$.

> **DEFINITION 1–1.** Two sets $A$ and $B$ are said to be *equal*, written $A = B$, if and only if every element of $A$ is an element of $B$ and every element of $B$ is an element of $A$. That is, $A = B$ provided $A$ and $B$ have the same elements.

Thus a set is completely determined by its elements. For instance,

$$\{1, 2, 3\} = \{3, 1, 2, 2\},$$

since each set contains only the integers 1, 2, and 3. Indeed, the order in which the elements are listed in a set is immaterial, and repetition conveys no additional information about the set.

An *empty set* or *null set*, represented by the symbol $\emptyset$, is any set containing no elements. For instance,

$$\emptyset = \{x \in R^{\#} \mid x^2 < 0\} \qquad \text{or} \qquad \emptyset = \{x \mid x \neq x\}.$$

Any two empty sets are equal, for in a trivial sense they both contain the same elements (namely, none). In effect, then, there is just one empty set, so that we are free to speak of "the empty set $\emptyset$."

The set whose only member is the element $x$ is called *singleton x* and denoted by $\{x\}$:

$$\{x\} = \{y \mid y = x\}.$$

In particular, $\{0\} \neq \emptyset$ since $0 \in \{0\}$.

> **DEFINITION 1–2.** The set $A$ is a *subset* of, or is *contained in* the set $B$, indicated by writing $A \subseteq B$, if every element of $A$ is also an element of $B$.

Our notation is designed to include the possibility that $A = B$. Whenever $A \subseteq B$ but $A \neq B$, we will write $A \subset B$ and say that $A$ is a *proper* subset of $B$.

It will be convenient to regard all sets under consideration as being subsets of some master set $U$, called the *universe* (universal set, ground set). While the universe may be different in different contexts, it will usually be fixed throughout any given discussion.

There are several immediate consequences of the definition of set inclusion.

**THEOREM 1-1.** If $A$, $B$, and $C$ are subsets of some universe $U$, then:

(a) $A \subseteq A$, $\emptyset \subseteq A$, $A \subseteq U$.

(b) $A \subseteq \emptyset$ if and only if $A = \emptyset$.

(c) $\{x\} \subseteq A$ if and only if $x \in A$; that is, each element of $A$ determines a subset of $A$.

(d) If $A \subseteq B$ and $B \subseteq C$, then $A \subseteq C$.

(e) $A \subseteq B$ and $B \subseteq A$ if and only if $A = B$.

Observe that the result $\emptyset \subseteq A$ follows from the logical principle that a false hypothesis implies any conclusion whatsoever. Thus, the statement, "if $x \in \emptyset$, then $x \in A$," is true since $x \in \emptyset$ is always false.

The last assertion of Theorem 1–1 indicates that a proof of the equality of two specified sets $A$ and $B$ is generally presented in two parts. One part demonstrates that if $x \in A$, then $x \in B$; the other part demonstrates that if $x \in B$, then $x \in A$. An illustration of such a proof will be given later.

We now consider several important ways in which sets may be combined with one another. If $A$ and $B$ are subsets of some universe $U$, the operations of union, intersection, and difference are defined as follows.

**DEFINITION 1–3.** The *union* of $A$ and $B$, denoted by $A \cup B$, is the subset of $U$ defined by

$$A \cup B = \{x \mid x \in A \quad \text{or} \quad x \in B\}.$$

The *intersection* of $A$ and $B$, denoted by $A \cap B$, is the subset of $U$ defined by

$$A \cap B = \{x \mid x \in A \quad \text{and} \quad x \in B\}.$$

The *difference* of $A$ and $B$ (sometimes called the *relative complement* of $B$ in $A$), denoted by $A - B$, is the subset of $U$ defined by

$$A - B = \{x \mid x \in A \quad \text{but} \quad x \notin B\}.$$

In the definition of union, the word "or" is used in the "and/or" sense. Thus the statement, "$x \in A$ or $x \in B$" includes the case where $x$ is in both $A$ and $B$.

The particular difference $U - B$ is called the (absolute) *complement* of $B$ and designated simply by $-B$. If $A$ and $B$ are two nonempty sets whose intersection is empty, that is, $A \cap B = \emptyset$, then they are said to be *disjoint*. We shall illustrate these concepts with an example.

EXAMPLE 1–1. Let the universe be $U = \{0, 1, 2, 3, 4, 5, 6\}$, $A = \{1, 2, 4\}$, and $B = \{2, 3, 5\}$.    Then $A \cup B = \{1, 2, 3, 4, 5\}$, $A \cap B = \{2\}$, $A - B = \{1, 4\}$, and $B - A = \{3, 5\}$.    Also, $-A = \{0, 3, 5, 6\}$, $-B = \{0, 1, 4, 6\}$.  Observe that $A - B$ and $B - A$ are unequal and disjoint.

In the following theorem are listed some simple consequences of the definitions of union, intersection, and complementation.

> **THEOREM 1–2.** If $A$, $B$, and $C$ are subsets of some universe $U$, then:
>
> (a) $A \cup A = A$, $A \cap A = A$;
> (b) $A \cup B = B \cup A$, $A \cap B = B \cap A$;
> (c) $A \cup (B \cup C) = (A \cup B) \cup C$,
>     $A \cap (B \cap C) = (A \cap B) \cap C$;
> (d) $A \cup (B \cap C) = (A \cup B) \cap (A \cup C)$,
>     $A \cap (B \cup C) = (A \cap B) \cup (A \cap C)$;
> (e) $A \cup \emptyset = A$, $A \cap \emptyset = \emptyset$;
> (f) $A \cup U = U$, $A \cap U = A$;
> (g) $A \cup (-A) = U$, $A \cap (-A) = \emptyset$.

We shall verify the first equality of (d), since its proof illustrates a technique mentioned previously.    Suppose that $x \in A \cup (B \cap C)$.    Then either $x \in A$ or $x \in B \cap C$.  Now, if $x \in A$, then clearly both $x \in A \cup B$ and $x \in A \cup C$, so that $x \in (A \cup B) \cap (A \cup C)$.    On the other hand, if $x \in B \cap C$, then $x \in B$ and therefore $x \in A \cup B$; also $x \in C$ and therefore $x \in A \cup C$.  The two conditions together imply

$$x \in (A \cup B) \cap (A \cup C).$$

This establishes the inclusion

$$A \cup (B \cap C) \subseteq (A \cup B) \cap (A \cup C).$$

Conversely, suppose $x \in (A \cup B) \cap (A \cup C)$.  Then both $x \in A \cup B$ and $x \in A \cup C$.  Since $x \in A \cup B$, either $x \in A$ or $x \in B$; at the same time, since $x \in A \cup C$, either $x \in A$ or $x \in C$.  Together, these conditions mean that $x \in A$ or $x \in B \cap C$; that is, $x \in A \cup (B \cap C)$.  This proves the opposite inclusion

$$(A \cup B) \cap (A \cup C) \subseteq A \cup (B \cap C).$$

By Part (e) of Theorem 1–1, the two inclusions are sufficient to establish the equality

$$A \cup (B \cap C) = (A \cup B) \cap (A \cup C).$$

The next theorem relates the operation of complementation to the other operations of set theory.

**THEOREM 1-3.** Let $A$ and $B$ be subsets of the universe $U$. Then

(a) $-(A \cup B) = (-A) \cap (-B)$;
(b) $-(A \cap B) = (-A) \cup (-B)$;
(c) if $A \subseteq B$, then $(-B) \subseteq (-A)$;
(d) $-(-A) = A$, $-\emptyset = U$, $-U = \emptyset$.

The first two parts of the above theorem are commonly known as DeMorgan's rules.

One final comment on set theory. It is both desirable and possible to extend our definitions of union and intersection from two sets to any number of sets. Suppose to this end that $\mathcal{C}$ is a nonempty collection of subsets of the universe $U$. The union and intersection of this arbitrary collection are defined by

$$\cup \mathcal{C} = \{x \mid x \in A \text{ for some set } A \in \mathcal{C}\},$$
$$\cap \mathcal{C} = \{x \mid x \in A \text{ for every set } A \in \mathcal{C}\}.$$

For instance, if $I_n = \{x \in R^{\#} \mid -1/n \leq x \leq 1/n\}$ for $n = 1, 2, \ldots$ and $\mathcal{C}$ is the collection of all the $I_n$, then

$$\cup \mathcal{C} = \{x \in R^{\#} \mid -1 \leq x \leq 1\}, \qquad \cap \mathcal{C} = \{0\}.$$

## PROBLEMS

In the following exercises $A$, $B$, and $C$ are subsets of some universe $U$.

1. Prove that $A \cap B \subseteq A \cup B$.
2. Suppose $A \subseteq B$. Show that
   (a) $A \cap C \subseteq B \cap C$          (b) $A \cup C \subseteq B \cup C$
3. Prove that $A - B = A \cap (-B)$, and use this result to verify each of the following identities:
   (a) $A - \emptyset = A$, $\emptyset - A = \emptyset$, $A - A = \emptyset$
   (b) $A - B = A - (A \cap B) = (A \cup B) - B$
   (c) $(A - B) \cap (B - A) = \emptyset$
4. Simplify the following expressions to one of the symbols $A$, $B$, $A \cup B$, $A \cap B$, $A - B$.
   (a) $A \cap (A \cup B)$      (b) $A - (A - B)$      (c) $-((A \cap B) \cup (-A))$
5. Prove that $A \cap (B \cup C) = (A \cap B) \cup (A \cap C)$.

6. Establish the following results on differences:

(a) $(A - B) - C = A - (B \cup C)$
(b) $A - (B - C) = (A - B) \cup (A \cap C)$
(c) $A \cup (B - C) = (A \cup B) - (C - A)$
(d) $A \cap (B - C) = (A \cap B) - (A \cap C)$

7. The notion of set inclusion may be expressed either in terms of union or intersection. To see this, prove that

(a) $A \subseteq B$ if and only if $A \cup B = B$,
(b) $A \subseteq B$ if and only if $A \cap B = A$.

## 1-2.  FUNCTIONS

From our definition of set equality, $\{a, b\} = \{b, a\}$, since both sets contain the same two elements $a$ and $b$. That is, no preference is given to one element over the other. When we wish to distinguish one of these elements as being the first, say $a$, we write $(a, b)$ and call this an ordered pair.

It is possible to give a purely set-theoretic definition of the notion of ordered pair as follows:

> **DEFINITION 1–4.**  The *ordered pair* of elements $a$ and $b$, with first component $a$ and second component $b$, denoted by $(a, b)$, is the set
>
> $$(a, b) = \big\{ \{a, b\}, \{a\} \big\}.$$

Note that, according to this definition, $a$ and $b$ are not elements of $(a, b)$ but rather components. The actual elements of the set $(a, b)$ are $\{a, b\}$, the unordered pair involved, and $\{a\}$, that member of the unordered pair which has been selected to be "first." Clearly this agrees with our intuition that an ordered pair should be an entity representing two elements in a given order.

For $a \neq b$, the sets $\big\{ \{a, b\}, \{a\} \big\}$ and $\big\{ \{b, a\}, \{b\} \big\}$ are unequal, having different elements, so that $(a, b) \neq (b, a)$. Hence, if $a$ and $b$ are distinct, there are two distinct ordered pairs whose components are $a$ and $b$: namely, the pairs $(a, b)$ and $(b, a)$. Ordered pairs thus provide a way of handling two things as one while losing track of neither. We emphasize again that there is just one set whose elements are $a$ and $b$, for $\{a, b\} = \{b, a\}$. As a consequence of Definition 1–4, it can be shown that

$$(a, b) = (c, d) \quad \text{if and only if} \quad a = c, \, b = d.$$

**DEFINITION 1–5.** The *Cartesian product* of two nonempty sets $A$ and $B$, designated by $A \times B$, is the set

$$A \times B = \{(a, b) \mid a \in A \text{ and } b \in B\}.$$

Whenever we employ the Cartesian product notation, it will be with the understanding that the sets involved are nonempty, even though this may not be explicitly stated at the time. Observe that if the set $A$ contains $n$ elements and $B$ contains $m$ elements, then $A \times B$ has $nm$ elements, which accounts for the use of the word "product" in Cartesian product.

EXAMPLE 1–2. Let $A = \{-1, 0, 1\}$ and $B = \{0, 2\}$. Then

$$A \times B = \{(-1, 0), (-1, 2), (0, 0), (0, 2), (1, 0), (1, 2)\}$$

while

$$B \times A = \{(0, -1), (0, 0), (0, 1), (2, -1), (2, 0), (2, 1)\}.$$

Clearly the sets $A \times B \neq B \times A$. In general, $A \times B = B \times A$ if and only if $A = B$.

We avoid the traditional view of a function as a rule of correspondence and instead give the following definition in terms of ordered pairs.

**DEFINITION 1–6.** A *function* (or *mapping*) $f$ is a set of ordered pairs such that no two distinct pairs have the same first component. Thus $(x, y_1) \in f$ and $(x, y_2) \in f$ implies $y_1 = y_2$.

The collection of all first components of a function $f$ is called the *domain* of the function and is denoted by $D_f$, while the collection of all second components is called the *range* of the function and is denoted by $R_f$. In terms of set notation,

$$D_f = \{x \mid (x, y) \in f \text{ for some } y\},$$
$$R_f = \{y \mid (x, y) \in f \text{ for some } x\}.$$

If $f$ is a function and $(x, y) \in f$, then $y$ is called the *functional value* or *image of $f$ at $x$* and is denoted by $f(x)$. That is, the symbol $f(x)$ represents the unique second component of that ordered pair of $f$ in which $x$ is the first component.

EXAMPLE 1–3. If the function $f$ is the finite set of ordered pairs

$$f = \{(-1, 0), (0, 0), (1, 2), (2, 1)\},$$

then

$$D_f = \{-1, 0, 1, 2\}, \qquad R_f = \{0, 1, 2\}$$

and we write $f(-1) = 0, f(0) = 0, f(1) = 2$ and $f(2) = 1$.

Quite often we describe a function by giving a formula for its ordered pairs. For instance, $f = \{(x, x^2 + 2) \mid x \in R^{\#}\}$. Using the functional value notation, we would then write

$$f(x) = x^2 + 2 \qquad \text{for} \qquad x \in R^{\#}.$$

**DEFINITION 1–7.**    If $f \subseteq X \times Y$, so that $D_f \subseteq X$ and $R_f \subseteq Y$, then $f$ is referred to as a function from $X$ *into* $Y$. In particular, if $D_f = X$, we will employ the notation

$$f \colon X \to Y.$$

The function $f$ is said to be *onto* $Y$, or an *onto function*, whenever $f$ is a function from $X$ into $Y$ and $R_f = Y$. Thus $f$ is onto $Y$ if and only if for each $y \in Y$ there exists some $x \in D_f$ with $(x, y) \in f$, so that $y = f(x)$.

Since functions are sets, we have a ready-made definition of equality of functions: two functions $f$ and $g$ are *equal* if and only if they have the same members. Accordingly, $f = g$ if and only if $D_f = D_g$ and $f(x) = g(x)$ for each element $x$ in their common domain.

Suppose that $f$ and $g$ are two specific functions. The following formulas define functions $f + g, f - g, f \cdot g$ and $f/g$ by specifying the value of these functions at each point of their domain:

$$\left. \begin{aligned} (f + g)(x) &= f(x) + g(x), \\ (f - g)(x) &= f(x) - g(x), \\ (f \cdot g)(x) &= f(x)g(x), \end{aligned} \right\} \qquad \text{where} \qquad x \in D_f \cap D_g,$$

$$(f/g)(x) = f(x)/g(x),$$

$$\text{where} \qquad x \in (D_f \cap D_g) - \{x \in D_g \mid g(x) = 0\}.$$

We term $f + g, f - g, f \cdot g$ and $f/g$, the *sum, difference, product,* and *quotient* of $f$ and $g$ respectively. Clearly the definitions of these functions make sense only when $R_f$ and $R_g$ are subsets of systems in which addition, subtraction, multiplication, and division are permissible.

EXAMPLE 1–4.    Suppose $f = \{(x, \sqrt{4 - x^2}) \mid -2 \le x \le 2\}$ and $g = \{(x, 2/x) \mid R^{\#} - \{0\}\}$, so that $f(x) = \sqrt{4 - x^2}$, $g(x) = 2/x$. Then for $x \in D_f \cap D_g = D_f - \{0\}$,

$$(f + g)(x) = \sqrt{4 - x^2} + \frac{2}{x},$$

$$(f - g)(x) = \sqrt{4 - x^2} - \frac{2}{x},$$

$$(f \cdot g)(x) = (\sqrt{4 - x^2})\frac{2}{x},$$

$$(f/g)(x) = \frac{\sqrt{4 - x^2}}{2/x} = \frac{x}{2}\sqrt{4 - x^2}.$$

**DEFINITION 1–8.** The *composition* of two functions $f$ and $g$, denoted by $f \circ g$, is the function

$$f \circ g = \{(x, y) \mid \text{for some } z, (x, z) \in g \quad \text{and} \quad (z, y) \in f\}.$$

Written in terms of functional values, we have

$$(f \circ g)(x) = f(g(x)), \quad \text{where} \quad x \in D_g \text{ and } g(x) \in D_f.$$

This last notation serves to explain the order of symbols in $f \circ g$; $g$ is written directly beside $x$, since the functional value $g(x)$ is obtained first. It is apparent from the definition that, so long as $R_g \cap D_f \neq \emptyset$, $f \circ g$ is meaningful. Also, $D_{f \circ g} \subseteq D_g$ and $R_{f \circ g} \subseteq R_f$.

EXAMPLE 1–5. Let

$$f = \{(x, \sqrt{x}) \mid x \in R^{\#}, x \geq 0\}$$

and

$$g = \{(x, 2x + 3) \mid x \in R^{\#}\},$$

so that $f(x) = \sqrt{x}$, $g(x) = 2x + 3$. Then,

$$(f \circ g)(x) = f(g(x)) = f(2x + 3) = \sqrt{2x + 3},$$

where

$$D_{f \circ g} = \{x \in D_g \mid g(x) \in D_f\} = \{x \in R^{\#} \mid 2x + 3 \in D_f\}$$
$$= \{x \mid 2x + 3 \geq 0\}.$$

On the other hand,

$$(g \circ f)(x) = g(f(x)) = g(\sqrt{x}) = 2\sqrt{x} + 3,$$

where

$$D_{g \circ f} = \{x \in D_f \mid f(x) \in D_g\} = \{x \geq 0 \mid \sqrt{x} \in R^{\#}\}$$
$$= \{x \mid x \geq 0\}.$$

One observes that $f \circ g$ is different from $g \circ f$; indeed, rarely does it happen that $f \circ g = g \circ f$.

The next theorem concerns some of the basic properties of the operation of functional composition. Its proof is an exercise in the use of the definitions of this section.

**THEOREM 1–4.** If $f$, $g$, and $h$ are functions for which the following operations are defined, then

(1) $(f \circ g) \circ h = f \circ (g \circ h)$,
(2) $(f + g) \circ h = (f \circ h) + (g \circ h)$,
(3) $(f \cdot g) \circ h = (f \circ h) \cdot (g \circ h)$.

*Proof.* We establish here only property (3). The other parts of the theorem are obtained in a similar fashion and so are left as an exercise. Observe first that

$$
\begin{aligned}
D_{(f \cdot g) \circ h} &= \{x \in D_h \mid h(x) \in D_{f \cdot g}\} \\
&= \{x \in D_h \mid h(x) \in D_f \cap D_g\} \\
&= \{x \in D_h \mid h(x) \in D_f\} \cap \{x \in D_h \mid h(x) \in D_g\} \\
&= D_{f \circ h} \cap D_{g \circ h} = D_{(f \circ h) \cdot (g \circ h)}.
\end{aligned}
$$

Now, for $x \in D_{(f \cdot g) \circ h}$, we have

$$
\begin{aligned}
[(f \cdot g) \circ h](x) &= (f \cdot g)\big(h(x)\big) = f\big(h(x)\big) \cdot g\big(h(x)\big) \\
&= (f \circ h)(x) \cdot (g \circ h)(x) \\
&= [(f \circ h) \cdot (g \circ h)](x),
\end{aligned}
$$

which, according to the definition of equality of functions, shows that

$$
(f \cdot g) \circ h = (f \circ h) \cdot (g \circ h).
$$

**DEFINITION 1–9.** A function $f$ is termed *one-to-one* if and only if $x_1, x_2 \in D_f$, with $x_1 \neq x_2$, implies $f(x_1) \neq f(x_2)$. That is, distinct elements in the domain have distinct functional values.

When establishing one-to-oneness, it will often prove to be more convenient to use the contrapositive of Definition 1–9:

$$
f(x_1) = f(x_2) \qquad \text{implies} \qquad x_1 = x_2.
$$

In terms of ordered pairs, a function $f$ is one-to-one if and only if no two distinct ordered pairs of $f$ have the same second component. Thus the collection of ordered pairs obtained by interchanging the components of the pairs of $f$ also results in a function. This observation indicates the importance of such functions.

More specifically, the *inverse* of a one-to-one function $f$, symbolized by $f^{-1}$, is the set of ordered pairs

$$
f^{-1} = \{(y, x) \mid (x, y) \in f\}.
$$

The function $f^{-1}$ has the properties

$$
\begin{aligned}
(f^{-1} \circ f)(x) &= x \qquad \text{for} \qquad x \in D_f, \\
(f \circ f^{-1})(y) &= y \qquad \text{for} \qquad y \in D_{f^{-1}} = R_f,
\end{aligned}
$$

so that $f^{-1}$ may be considered the inverse of $f$ with respect to composition.

EXAMPLE 1–6. The function $f = \{(x, 3x - 2) \mid x \in R^{\#}\}$ is one-to-one, for $3x_1 - 2 = 3x_2 - 2$ implies $x_1 = x_2$. Consequently, the inverse of $f$ exists and is the set of ordered pairs $f^{-1} = \{(3x - 2, x) \mid x \in R^{\#}\}$. It is preferable, however, to have $f^{-1}$ defined in terms of its domain and the value at each point of the domain. Observing that

$$\{(3x - 2, x) \mid x \in R^{\#}\} = \{(x, \tfrac{1}{3}(x + 2)) \mid x \in R^{\#}\},$$

we choose to write $f^{-1} = \{(x, \tfrac{1}{3}(x + 2)) \mid x \in R^{\#}\}$. In terms of functional values, $f^{-1}(x) = \tfrac{1}{3}(x + 2)$ for each $x \in R^{\#}$.

Let us conclude with a definition regarding a frequently employed notation.

> **DEFINITION 1–10.** Consider a function $f: X \to Y$. If $A \subseteq X$, then the *direct image* of $A$, symbolized by $f(A)$, is the subset of $Y$ defined by
>
> $f(A) = \{f(x) \mid x \in A\}.$

On the other hand, if $B \subseteq Y$, then the *inverse image* of $B$, symbolized by $f^{-1}(B)$, is the subset of $X$ defined by

$$f^{-1}(B) = \{x \mid f(x) \in B\}.$$

# PROBLEMS

1. For sets $A$, $B \subseteq X$ and $C$, $D \subseteq Y$, verify the following properties of the Cartesian product:
   (a) $(A \cap B) \times (C \cap D) = (A \times C) \cap (B \times D)$
   (b) $(A - B) \times C = (A \times C) - (B \times C)$

2. Determine $f \circ g$, $g \circ f$, and their respective domains, given
   (a) $f = \{(x, x^2 + x) \mid x \in R^{\#}\}, \quad g = \{(x, 3x + 4) \mid x \in R^{\#}\}$
   (b) $f = \{(x, (x - 1)/(x^2 - 9)) \mid x \in R^{\#} - \{3, -3\}\},$
       $g = \{(x, 2x - 1) \mid x \in R^{\#}\}$

3. Verify the law $f \circ (g \circ h) = (f \circ g) \circ h$.

4. Determine which of the following functions are one-to-one. In those cases where the function $f$ is not one-to-one, exhibit two pairs $(x_1, y_1)$, $(x_2, y_2) \in f$ such that $x_1 \neq x_2$, but $y_1 = y_2$.
   (a) $f = \{(x, 2x + 3) \mid x \in R_{+}^{\#}\}$      (b) $f = \{(x, x^2 + 1) \mid x \in R^{\#}\}$
   (c) $f = \{(x, \sqrt{x}) \mid x \in R_{+}^{\#}\}$         (d) $f = \{(x, |x - 1|) \mid -2 \leq x \leq 2\}$.

5. Show that the function $f = \{(x, x/(x - 1)) \mid -1 \leq x < 1\}$ is one-to-one and obtain its inverse.

6. Prove that if $f$ and $g$ are both one-to-one functions, then $f \circ g$ is also one-to-one, and $(f \circ g)^{-1} = g^{-1} \circ f^{-1}$.

7. For functions $f$ and $g$, with domain $R^{\#}$, define

$$f \triangledown g = (f \circ g) - (g \circ f).$$

   (a) What is the domain of $f \triangledown g$?
   (b) Show that $(f \triangledown g) + (g \triangledown f) = 0$, where $0$ is the function for which $0(x) = 0$ for all $x \in R^{\#}$.

8. If $f$ and $g$ are functions having domain $R^{\#}$, let $f \vee g$ be the function given by $(f \vee g)(x) = \text{maximum } \{f(x), g(x)\}$. Determine whether or not $f \vee g$ is a one-to-one function.

9. Given $f \colon X \to Y$ and $A, B \subseteq X$, show that
   (a) $f(A \cup B) = f(A) \cup f(B)$, but $f(A \cap B) \subseteq f(A) \cap f(B)$
   (b) $f(A - B) \supseteq f(A) - f(B)$

*Chapter 2*

# SYSTEMS WITH
# A SINGLE OPERATION

## 2-1. DEFINITION AND EXAMPLES
## OF GROUPS

In the present chapter, and throughout the remainder of the text, we will deal with mathematical systems which are defined by sets of postulates. By working in this general setting—that is, with an axiomatically defined concept—we are able to concentrate on the essential features of the object under consideration and to illuminate a variety of classical examples by displaying them in an abstract context.

We begin with one-operational systems, since they lend themselves to the simplest formal description. Despite this simplicity, the axioms permit the construction of a profuse and elegant theory in which we will encounter many of the fundamental notions common to all algebraic systems.

Most sets dealt with in mathematics are sets which have an "algebraic structure," meaning that certain suitably restricted rules of combination or operations are defined on them. These rules enable us to combine the elements of the sets in useful ways. Our aim is to study the common patterns of algebraic structure which underly many diverse and seemingly unrelated examples.

If $a$ and $b$ are elements of some set $S$ under consideration, then $a * b$ shall denote the result of combining $a$ with $b$ according to whatever rule of combination $*$ we wish to investigate. The notation $a * b$ is to be read as either "$a$ star $b$" or "$a$ combined with $b$." The particular symbol used for the abstract product of elements is of no great importance; there will be times when we choose to write $a \circ b$ instead of $a * b$. In general, $a$ and $b$ will not represent numbers but simply arbitrary elements in our underlying set $S$, whatever this set may be, while $*$ may well be some odd rule of combination which bears no resemblance to the usual operations of elementary algebra.

We will take the equality sign "$=$" intuitively to mean "is the same as." That is, $=$ asserts that the two particular expressions involved are merely different names for, or descriptions of, one and the same object; just one object is being considered, and it is named twice. To indicate that $a$ and $b$ are not the same object, we will write $a \neq b$.

EXAMPLE 2–1. Suppose that the set $S$ were to consist of the pairs of initials of a certain group of people (first and last names only). A possible rule of combination $*$ for this set is defined as follows: to combine one set of initials with another we form a pair whose first letter is the first letter in the first pair of initials and whose second letter is the second letter in the second pair of initials. For instance, if $(D, B)$ and $(P, Q)$ are elements of $S$, then

$$(D, B) * (P, Q) = (D, Q).$$

EXAMPLE 2–2. Let $S = Z_+$, the positive integers. A rule of combination $*$ could be given by the formula

$$a * b = a \cdot b^2, \qquad a, b \in Z_+.$$

(We shall denote the product of $a$ and $b$ under ordinary multiplication by $a \cdot b$ or $ab$.)

There is certainly no reason to expect that $b * a$ will be the same as $a * b$. In fact, one sees in the last example that

$$2 * 3 = 2 \cdot (3)^2 = 18,$$

whereas

$$3 * 2 = 3 \cdot (2)^2 = 12.$$

We should also observe that it is quite possible to combine an element with itself; that is, $a * a$ can be defined.

When the set being considered has a relatively small number of elements, the results of applying the rule of combination to its members may be conveniently represented in tabular form. We construct this table by first listing the members of $S$ both vertically and horizontally. The result $a * b$ appears in the body of the table at the intersection of the row headed by $a$ and the column headed by $b$. Such a table could equally well serve to define a rule of combination on $S$, for the result of combining every pair of elements of $S$ would appear somewhere in the table.

EXAMPLE 2–3. A rule of correspondence may be defined on the set $S = \{a, b, c\}$ by the following *operation* (or *multiplication*) *table:*

| * | a | b | c |
|---|---|---|---|
| a | a | b | c |
| b | b | c | a |
| c | c | a | b |

According to the table, $b * c = a$, $c * a = b * b$ (both equal to $c$), and so on.

There are certain desirable features that a rule of combination * should possess. In the first place, it should always be possible to apply the rule to any two members $a$ and $b$ of the set $S$ under investigation, and to obtain a unique, unambiguous result. We would further like the result of combining any two members of the set $S$ to be again a member of $S$; that is, we want $a * b \in S$ whenever $a, b \in S$. This would permit us to apply the rule once more and combine $a * b$ with other elements of $S$.

The last requirement is known as the closure property, and when it holds we say the set $S$ is *closed* under the rule of combination *. When the features mentioned in the last paragraph are present, then the rule of combination is called a *binary operation*, or merely an *operation*. The formal definition follows.

**DEFINITION 2–1.** A *binary operation* on a nonempty set $S$ is any rule of combination * which assigns to each ordered pair $(a, b)$ of elements of $S$ a uniquely determined element $a * b$ of the same set $S$.

Note that in view of Section 1–2, a binary operation on a set $S$ could be interpreted as a function from the Cartesian product $S \times S$ to the set $S$.

By a *mathematical* (or *algebraic*) *system*, we shall mean a set of elements together with one or more binary operations defined on this set. The systems subsequently to be considered shall be classified according to the properties they possess. Such a classification leads to that branch of mathematics known as Abstract Algebra. Our object is to give a logical development of mathematical systems beginning with those with relatively little algebraic structure and progressing to systems rich in structure.

**DEFINITION 2–2.** A mathematical system $(S, *)$ consisting of a nonempty set $S$ of arbitrary elements together with a single binary operation * defined on $S$ is called a *groupoid*.

A groupoid is determined not by its set of elements alone, but by the set together with the binary operation defined on it. Thus different groupoids may well have the same associated set of elements, and this is the reason for defining a groupoid as an ordered pair of things.

EXAMPLE 2–4. The pair $(Z_+, -)$, where the underlying set is the positive integers and the operation that of ordinary subtraction, does not constitute a groupoid, for the set $Z_+$ is clearly not closed with respect to subtraction. The pair $(Z_+, +)$, however, forms a groupoid.

EXAMPLE 2–5. If $Z_o$ denotes the odd integers, then $(Z_o, +)$ is not a groupoid.

A set on which a single binary operation is defined does not by itself yield a structure rich enough for our purpose. The concept, being too general, is poor in content. Certain requirements on the operation are necessary if we are to derive useful results. In the following paragraphs we shall name these requirements and briefly examine them.

At the moment, the symbol $a * b * c$ is completely meaningless, since the operation $*$ has been defined only for pairs of elements. If, however, we make the stipulation that whenever quantities are enclosed in parentheses these are to be evaluated first, then the expressions $a * (b * c)$ and $(a * b) * c$ do take on meaning. Thus $a * (b * c)$ is to be interpreted as

combine $a$ with what results from combining $b$ with $c$,

while $(a * b) * c$ is to be interpreted as

first combine $a$ with $b$ and then combine the result with $c$.

**DEFINITION 2–3.** The operation $*$ defined on the set $S$ is said to be *associative* if

$$a * (b * c) = (a * b) * c$$

for every triple of elements $a$, $b$, and $c$ of $S$.

EXAMPLE 2–6. The operation of subtraction on the set $R^{\#}$ of real numbers is not associative, since clearly

$$a - (b - c) \neq (a - b) - c.$$

EXAMPLE 2–7. Define an operation $*$ on the set of integers $Z$ by the formula

$$a * b = a + b + 1.$$

Then $*$ is an associative operation, for

$$a * (b * c) = a * (b + c + 1) = a + (b + c + 1) + 1$$
$$= a + b + c + 2$$

and

$$(a * b) * c = (a + b + 1) * c = (a + b + 1) + c + 1$$
$$= a + b + c + 2.$$

EXAMPLE 2–8. Another operation $*$ on the real numbers which is associative is given by the rule

$$a * b = \max \{a, b\}, \qquad \text{where } a, b \in R^{\#}.$$

That is, $a * b$ is the larger of the elements $a$ and $b$, or either one if $a = b$. Thus $a * (b * c) = \max \{a, b, c\} = (a * b) * c$.

When dealing with a groupoid whose operation is defined by a multiplication table rather than a formula, it is generally quite tedious to establish the associativity of the operation, since one must show

$$a * (b * c) = (a * b) * c$$

for all possible choices of $a$, $b$, and $c$ from the underlying set. On the other hand, it may be easy to show that the operation is not associative, since then all we need do is find three particular elements for which the associative law fails.

EXAMPLE 2–9. Consider the operation $*$ defined on the set $S = \{1, 2, 3\}$ by the operation table:

| $*$ | 1 | 2 | 3 |
|---|---|---|---|
| 1 | 1 | 2 | 3 |
| 2 | 3 | 1 | 2 |
| 3 | 2 | 3 | 1 |

From this table, we see that $2 * (1 * 3) = 2 * 3 = 2$, while $(2 * 1) * 3 = 3 * 3 = 1$; that is,

$$2 * (1 * 3) \neq (2 * 1) * 3.$$

The associative law thus fails to hold in this groupoid $(S, *)$.

The mathematical system which we shall use to build up more complicated algebraic structures is known as a semigroup.

> **DEFINITION 2–4.** A *semigroup* is a groupoid whose operation satisfies the associative law. That is, a semigroup is a pair $(S, *)$ consisting of a nonempty set $S$ and an associative binary operation $*$ defined on $S$.

Observe that since any three elements from the underlying set of a semigroup always associate, there is no particular reason for parentheses. Consequently, when dealing with such a system, the symbol $a * b * c$ has meaning in the sense that we are free to interpret it as either $a * (b * c)$ or $(a * b) * c$.

In order to solidify the notion of semigroup we shall present a variety of examples.

EXAMPLE 2–10.  $(Z, +)$ and $(Z, \cdot)$ are both semigroups, while $(Z, -)$ is not.

EXAMPLE 2–11.  If the operation $*$ is defined on $R^\#$ by $a * b = \max\{a, b\}$, then Example 2–8 shows $(R^\#, *)$ to be a semigroup.

EXAMPLE 2–12.  Let $S_U$ denote the collection of all subsets of some given universe $U$. Each of the systems $(S_U, \cup)$ and $(S_U, \cap)$ constitutes a semigroup (see Theorem 1–2).

EXAMPLE 2–13.  Another example is provided by the set $S = \{0, 1\}$ and the operation $*$ determined from the table:

| $*$ | 0 | 1 |
|---|---|---|
| 0 | 0 | 0 |
| 1 | 1 | 1 |

We leave to the reader the verification that $(S, *)$ is actually a semigroup.

In general, the order in which elements occur in a product is quite essential. If it is possible to interchange the order of combining any two elements from our set without affecting the result, then the operation is termed commutative.

> **DEFINITION 2–5.**  The operation $*$ defined on the set $S$ is said to be *commutative* if
>
> $$a * b = b * a$$
>
> for every pair of elements $a, b \in S$.

The first three examples listed above are commutative semigroups— semigroups whose operation is commutative—while in the last example $0 * 1 = 0 \neq 1 = 1 * 0$, so the commutative law fails in that particular system.

Once an operation is defined on a set, we often find that certain elements play special roles: there may exist "identity elements" and "inverse elements."

> **DEFINITION 2–6.**  A groupoid $(S, *)$ is said to have a (two-sided) *identity element for the operation* $*$ if there exists an element $e$ in $S$ such that
>
> $$a * e = e * a = a$$
>
> for every $a \in S$. An element $e$ having this property is called an identity element (unit element, neutral element).

Thus an identity element causes each element of the set $S$ to remain "stationary" under the operation. In particular, observe that $e * e = e$. The following theorem establishes a fact which we shall need later.

**THEOREM 2–1.** A groupoid has at most one identity element.

*Proof.* Let us suppose that the groupoid $(S, *)$ has two identity elements $e$ and $e'$. Since $e * a = a$ for each $a \in S$, then, in particular $e * e' = e'$. But, on the other hand, $e'$ is also an identity element; so we must have $e * e' = e$. We thus obtain $e = e * e' = e'$ and consequently $e = e'$; that is, if the groupoid has an identity, then there is precisely one element with this property.

**DEFINITION 2–7.** A semigroup $(S, *)$ having an identity element for the operation $*$ is called a *monoid*.

EXAMPLE 2–14. The semigroup $(Z_+, \cdot)$ has an identity element for the operation of ordinary multiplication, namely, the positive integer 1; the semigroup $(Z_+, +)$ has none, since $0 \notin Z_+$.

EXAMPLE 2–15. Both the semigroups $(S_U, \cup)$ and $(S_U, \cap)$ are instances of monoids. Here, the empty set $\emptyset$ is the identity element for the union operation, since

$$A \cup \emptyset = \emptyset \cup A = A \quad \text{for each} \quad A \subseteq U,$$

while the universal set $U$ serves as the identity for the operation of intersection, since

$$A \cap U = U \cap A = A \quad \text{for each} \quad A \subseteq U.$$

EXAMPLE 2–16. As another example of a monoid, consider the set of numbers

$$S = \{a + b\sqrt{2} \mid a, b \in Z\}$$

and the operation of ordinary multiplication. First, one must check that $S$ is actually closed under multiplication; this is fairly evident, for if $a + b\sqrt{2}$ and $c + d\sqrt{2}$ are arbitrary members of $S$, then

$$(a + b\sqrt{2})(c + d\sqrt{2}) = (ac + 2bd) + (ad + bc)\sqrt{2} \in S.$$

It is not particularly difficult to establish that this system is a commutative semigroup with identity element $1 = 1 + 0\sqrt{2}$; that is, it is a commutative monoid. We shall omit the argument.

When dealing with an operation which has an identity element, it is natural to inquire which elements of the underlying set, if any, have "inverses."

> **DEFINITION 2-8.** Let $(S, *)$ be a groupoid with identity element $e$. An element $a \in S$ is said to have a (two-sided) *inverse under the operation* $*$ if there exists some member $a'$ of $S$ such that
>
> $$a * a' = a' * a = e.$$
>
> An element $a'$ having this property is called an inverse of $a$ and is customarily denoted by $a^{-1}$.

An inverse thus reduces a given element to the identity element under the operation. In particular, since $e * e = e$, we infer that $e^{-1} = e$. A further useful conclusion to be drawn from Definition 2-8 is that $(a^{-1})^{-1} = a$. A word of caution: the symbol $a^{-1}$ is used to denote the inverse of an element $a$ and is not to be confused with the reciprocal $1/a$.

We shall establish shortly that for a monoid, each element has at most one inverse with respect to the unique identity element. In dealing with monoids, we are free thus to speak of "the inverse of an element."

EXAMPLE 2-17. Let $S$ be the set of all ordered pairs of nonzero real numbers and $*$ the binary operation defined on $S$ by

$$(a, b) * (c, d) = (ac, bd).$$

It follows that the system $(S, *)$ is a commutative monoid having the pair $(1, 1)$ as its identity element. For an element $(a, b) \in S$,

$$(a, b)^{-1} = (1/a, 1/b),$$

since

$$(a, b) * (1/a, 1/b) = (a(1/a), b(1/b)) = (1, 1).$$

Observe that the value of the inverse varies from element to element; there is no "universal inverse."

EXAMPLE 2-18. In the commutative monoid $(S_U, \cup)$ of Example 2-15, only the empty set $\emptyset$ has an inverse. For if $A \in S_U$ and $A \neq \emptyset$, there is no subset $A^{-1}$ of $U$ such that $A \cup A^{-1} = \emptyset$. Similarly, in the case of the monoid $(S_U, \cap)$, the only element possessing an inverse is the universe $U$.

There is a mathematical system, known as a group, which displays most of the properties we have discussed.

**DEFINITION 2–9.** A pair $(G, *)$ is a *group* if and only if $(G, *)$ is a semigroup, with an identity, in which each element of $G$ has an inverse.

While this definition is perfectly acceptable, we prefer to rephrase it in the following more detailed form merely as a matter of convenience.

**DEFINITION 2–10.** A group is a pair $(G, *)$ consisting of a nonempty set $G$, and a rule of combination $*$ defined on ordered pairs of elements of $G$, satisfying the four requirements:

(1) $G$ is closed under the rule of combination $*$.

(2) The rule of combination $*$ is associative.

(3) $G$ contains an identity element $e$ for $*$.

(4) Each element $a$ of $G$ has an inverse $a^{-1} \in G$ with respect to $*$.

This definition calls for several remarks. If we had taken $*$ as a binary operation (rather than just a rule of combination), then the first of the above requirements could have been omitted, since any set is closed with respect to a binary operation defined on it. Observe also that commutativity is not required in the definition. If it happens that the group operation $*$ is commutative, then $(G, *)$ is referred to as a *commutative* (or *abelian*) *group*.

One must carefully distinguish the word "group" from the similar sounding words previously introduced, such as "groupoid" or "semigroup":

A groupoid must satisfy only the first of the conditions of Definition 2–10.

A semigroup must satisfy only the first two of the conditions of Definition 2–10.

A monoid must satisfy only the first three of the conditions of Definition 2–10.

A group, however, must satisfy all four.

When the group operation is clearly understood, we often identify the group with its underlying set of elements and refer to the group as $G$ rather than as $(G, *)$. For further simplicity, one frequently writes $ab$ for $a * b$. While we adhere to the $a * b$ notation, we will adopt some of the terminology of ordinary multiplication and speak of forming products, multiplying elements, etc. At times, we shall also be somewhat imprecise and talk about the elements of the group $(G, *)$, when we really mean the elements of the underlying set $G$; however, this should cause no real confusion.

In order to appreciate the generality of the concept of a group, and to gain some familiarity with this idea, we shall list several examples below.

EXAMPLE 2–19.  Let $a$ be any nonzero real number and consider the set $G$ of integral multiples of $a$:

$$G = \{na \mid n \in Z\}.$$

The pair $(G, +)$, where, as usual, $+$ indicates ordinary addition, forms a commutative group.  In this case, the identity is $0 = 0 \cdot a \in G$, while the inverse of an arbitrary element $na$ of $G$ is $-(na) = (-n)a \in G$.

EXAMPLE 2–20.  Consider the set of ordered pairs

$$G = \{(0, 0), (0, 1), (1, 0), (1, 1)\}$$

and the operation $*$ defined by Table 2–1. In this group, the identity element is the pair $(0, 0)$, and every element is its own inverse. Here the verification of the associative law becomes a process of detailed enumeration of all possible cases that could arise.

TABLE 2–1

| $*$ | $(0, 0)$ | $(0, 1)$ | $(1, 0)$ | $(1, 1)$ |
|---|---|---|---|---|
| $(0, 0)$ | $(0, 0)$ | $(0, 1)$ | $(1, 0)$ | $(1, 1)$ |
| $(0, 1)$ | $(0, 1)$ | $(0, 0)$ | $(1, 1)$ | $(1, 0)$ |
| $(1, 0)$ | $(1, 0)$ | $(1, 1)$ | $(0, 0)$ | $(0, 1)$ |
| $(1, 1)$ | $(1, 1)$ | $(1, 0)$ | $(0, 1)$ | $(0, 0)$ |

Since the entire table is symmetric about the main diagonal (upper left to lower right), the group operation $*$ is commutative. Note that each element of $G$ appears once and only once in each row and column of the table. Indeed, any multiplication table for a group has this feature.

EXAMPLE 2–21.  Let $G$ be the collection of all subsets of some nonempty universe $U$.  As we have seen, the systems $(G, \cup)$ and $(G, \cap)$ possess identity elements $\emptyset$ and $U$, respectively, but neither system has inverses for any elements other than their identity elements. Consequently $G$ does not constitute a group with respect to the formulation of either unions or intersections. It is possible, however, to define an operation on $G$ in terms of union and intersection that will result in a group.

More specifically, consider the operation $*$ given by the formula

$$A * B = (A - B) \cup (B - A), \qquad A, B \in G.$$

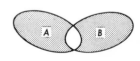

This operation, known as the *symmetric difference* of $A$ and $B$, yields the set which is represented by

Figure 2–1

the shaded area in Fig. 2–1. We shall leave the verification that the symmetric difference operation is commutative and associative as an exercise.

Clearly, for any set $A \subseteq U$ (that is, for any element of $G$),

$$A * \emptyset = (A - \emptyset) \cup (\emptyset - A) = A \cup \emptyset = A,$$

which proves that the empty set $\emptyset$ serves as an identity element for $*$. Also, $A * A = (A - A) \cup (A - A) = \emptyset \cup \emptyset = \emptyset$. This implies that each element of $G$ is its own inverse. Consequently, the algebraic system $(G, *)$ is a commutative group.

EXAMPLE 2–22. As an example of a noncommutative group, let the set $G$ consist of all ordered pairs of real numbers with nonzero first component:

$$G = \{(a, b) \mid a, b \in R^{\#}, a \neq 0\}.$$

Define the operation $*$ on $G$ by the formula

$$(a, b) * (c, d) = (ac, bc + d).$$

The associativity of the operation follows from the familiar properties of the real numbers, for we have

$$
\begin{aligned}
[(a, b) * (c, d)] * (e, f) &= (ac, bc + d) * (e, f) \\
&= ((ac)e, (bc + d)e + f) \\
&= (a(ce), b(ce) + (de + f)) \\
&= (a, b) * (ce, de + f) \\
&= (a, b) * [(c, d) * (e, f)].
\end{aligned}
$$

It is readily verified that the pair $(1, 0)$ serves as the identity element, while the inverse of $(a, b) \in G$ is $(1/a, -b/a)$. To see that the group $(G, *)$ is not commutative, merely consider the elements $(1, 2)$ and $(3, 4)$ of $G$:

$$(1, 2) * (3, 4) = (3, 10) \neq (3, 6) = (3, 4) * (1, 2).$$

EXAMPLE 2–23. As another example of a noncommutative group, take the set $G$ as consisting of the six functions $f_1, f_2, \ldots, f_6$, where for

$$x \in R^{\#} - \{0, 1\},$$

we define

$$f_1(x) = x, \qquad f_2(x) = \frac{1}{x}, \qquad f_3(x) = 1 - x,$$

$$f_4(x) = \frac{x - 1}{x}, \qquad f_5(x) = \frac{x}{x - 1}, \qquad f_6(x) = \frac{1}{1 - x},$$

with the group operation $*$ being that of functional composition (see Definition 1–8).

Thus, as an illustration, we have

$$(f_2 * f_6)(x) = f_2(f_6(x)) = f_2\left(\frac{1}{1-x}\right) = \frac{1}{1/(1-x)}$$
$$= 1 - x = f_3(x),$$

which implies that $f_2 * f_6 = f_3$. On the other hand,

$$(f_6 * f_2)(x) = f_6(f_2(x)) = f_6\left(\frac{1}{x}\right) = \frac{1}{1 - 1/x}$$
$$= \frac{x}{x-1} = f_5(x),$$

so that $f_6 * f_2 = f_5$, which shows that the operation $*$ is not commutative. The multiplication for $(G, *)$ in this case is defined by Table 2–2.

TABLE 2–2

| $*$ | $f_1$ | $f_2$ | $f_3$ | $f_4$ | $f_5$ | $f_6$ |
|-----|-------|-------|-------|-------|-------|-------|
| $f_1$ | $f_1$ | $f_2$ | $f_3$ | $f_4$ | $f_5$ | $f_6$ |
| $f_2$ | $f_2$ | $f_1$ | $f_6$ | $f_5$ | $f_4$ | $f_3$ |
| $f_3$ | $f_3$ | $f_4$ | $f_1$ | $f_2$ | $f_6$ | $f_5$ |
| $f_4$ | $f_4$ | $f_3$ | $f_5$ | $f_6$ | $f_2$ | $f_1$ |
| $f_5$ | $f_5$ | $f_6$ | $f_4$ | $f_3$ | $f_1$ | $f_2$ |
| $f_6$ | $f_6$ | $f_5$ | $f_2$ | $f_1$ | $f_3$ | $f_4$ |

Since functional composition is associative (Theorem 1–4), the system $(G, *)$ is certainly a semigroup. The operation table shows that $f_1$ is an identity element and the respective inverses are

$$f_1^{-1} = f_1, \quad f_2^{-1} = f_2, \quad f_3^{-1} = f_3, \quad f_4^{-1} = f_6,$$
$$f_5^{-1} = f_5, \quad f_6^{-1} = f_4.$$

To encompass all the different groups above in a single concept obviously requires the formulation of the underlying group concept in the most general terms. This is precisely the point we hope to convey to the reader: the value of contemporary mathematics lies in its power to abstract and thus to lay bare the structurally essential relations between superficially distinct entities.

Historically, the notion of a group arose early in the 19th century out of attempts to solve polynomial equations. Galois was the first to use the word "group" in any technical sense when he considered the group of permutations of the roots of such equations. A major achievement in the evolution of the theory was Klein's classification in the 1870's of the various branches of geometry according to groups of transformations under which certain geometric properties remain invariant. It remained some time however before satisfactory group postulates, free of redundancy, were stated. Definition 2–10, first formulated in 1902, is attributed to the American mathematician E. V. Huntington.

In the twentieth century, group theory has embraced all branches of mathematics and, indeed, a wide variety of other fields. It is difficult to give examples without becoming too technical, but the theory of groups is now employed in the study of quantum mechanics, general relativity, and crystallography. In these areas, group theory is not merely a tool with which calculations are made but also a source of concepts and principles for the formulation of new theories. A recent example can be found in the physics of fundamental particles with the discovery of a new "elementary particle" whose existence had been predicted from a classification scheme based on groups. It is certainly appropriate to begin our investigation of mathematical systems with this concept.

## PROBLEMS

1. Determine which of the following binary operations on the set $Z$ are associative and which are commutative:
   (a) $a * b = 0$                    (b) $a * b = \frac{1}{2}(a + b)$
   (c) $a * b = b$                    (d) $a * b = a + b - 1$

2. Let $(S, *)$ be a commutative semigroup. If $a, b, c \in S$, show that $a * (b * c) = c * (b * a)$.

3. Suppose the system $(S, *)$ is a groupoid with identity element $e$. Show that if the equation

   $$(a * b) * (c * d) = (a * c) * (b * d)$$

   holds for all possible choices of elements $a, b, c,$ and $d$ of $S$, then the operation $*$ is both associative and commutative.

4. Prove that the set of ordered pairs of real numbers together with the operation $*$ defined on $S$ by

   $$(a, b) * (c, d) = (a + c, b + d + 2bd)$$

   constitutes a commutative monoid.

5. Let us define a binary operation $*$ on the set $S = \{1, 2, 3, 4, 6\}$ as follows:

   $$a * b = \text{greatest common divisor of } a \text{ and } b.$$

   For example, $6 * 4 = 2, 3 * 4 = 1$, etc. Show that $(S, *)$ is a commutative monoid.

6. In the following instances, determine whether the systems $(G, *)$ described are commutative groups. For those systems failing to be so, indicate which axioms are not satisfied.

(a) $G = R^{\#}, a * b = ab$

(b) $G = Z, a * b = \min \{a, b\}$ (the smaller of $a$ and $b$)

(c) $G = R^{\#}, a * b = a + b - ab$

(d) $G = \{x \in R^{\#} \mid 0 \leq x \leq 1\}, a * b = \max \{\tfrac{1}{2}, ab\}$

(e) $G = \{1, 2, 3, \ldots, n\}$, where $n \geq 3$, $a * b = \begin{cases} a + b \text{ if } a + b \leq n \\ n \text{ if } a + b > n \end{cases}$

(f) $G = Z_+, a * b = \max \{a, b\} - \min \{a, b\}$

(g) $G = Z \times Z, (a, b) * (c, d) = (a + c, b + d)$

(h) $G = R^{\#} \times R^{\#}, (a, b) * (c, d) = (ac + bd, ad + bd)$

(i) $G = R^{\#} \times R^{\#} - \{(0, 0)\}, (a, b) * (c, d) = (ac - bd, ad + bc)$

7. Suppose that $a \in R^{\#} - \{0, 1\}$ and consider the set $G$ of integral powers of $a$: $G = \{a^k \mid k \in Z\}$. If $\cdot$ denotes ordinary multiplication, prove that $(G, \cdot)$ is a group.

8. Let $G = \{1, (-1 + i\sqrt{3})/2, (-1 - i\sqrt{3})/2\}$, where $i^2 = -1$. Show that the system $(G, \cdot)$ is a group.

9. Consider the set $G$ consisting of the four functions $f_1, f_2, f_3, f_4$:

$$f_1(x) = x, \qquad f_2(x) = \frac{1}{x}, \qquad f_3(x) = -x, \qquad f_4(x) = -\frac{1}{x}$$

for $x \in R^{\#} - \{0\}$. Prove that $(G, \circ)$ is a group, where $\circ$ denotes functional composition.

10. Prove that the symmetric difference operation $A * B = (A - B) \cup (B - A)$ discussed in Example 2–21 may also be defined by the formula

$$A * B = (A \cup B) - (A \cap B).$$

11. Show that the following two operation tables define groups:

| * | 1 | 3 | 5 | 7 |
|---|---|---|---|---|
| 1 | 1 | 3 | 5 | 7 |
| 3 | 3 | 1 | 7 | 5 |
| 5 | 5 | 7 | 1 | 3 |
| 7 | 7 | 5 | 3 | 1 |

| * | a | b | c | d |
|---|---|---|---|---|
| a | a | b | c | d |
| b | b | a | d | c |
| c | c | d | b | a |
| d | d | c | a | b |

12. A groupoid $(S, *)$ is said to have a *left identity element* for the operation $*$ if there exists an element $e \in S$ such that

$$e * a = a \qquad \text{for each} \qquad a \in S.$$

A *right identity element* is defined in an analogous manner. (a) Given $S = Z$, determine two right and one left identity elements for the operation $*$ given by $a * b = ab^2$. (b) Given $S = R^{\#} \times R^{\#}$, show that the operation $*$ defined on $S$ by the formula $(a, b) * (c, d) = (ac + bc, ad + bd)$ has two left identity elements but no right identity. (c) Prove that if the groupoid $(S, *)$ has a left identity element $e_1$ and a right identity element $e_2$, then $e_1 = e_2$.

## 2–2.  CERTAIN ELEMENTARY THEOREMS ON GROUPS

As we remarked earlier, our approach to the subject matter in this text is characterized by the abstract axiomatic development of modern mathematics. Thus each new system to be investigated consists of a set of elements and one or more operations which are undefined except that they are assumed to obey certain rules known as axioms or postulates. Once the axioms are granted, all else is obtained by careful logical argument. Each new theorem is deduced from the definitions, the axioms, and the theorems previously proven. The great advantage of the axiomatic method is that any particular example we encounter which satisfies the axioms of a given mathematical system will also satisfy all the theorems which are true for that system. While the uninitiated reader may find this approach uncomfortably abstract at first, the feeling will disappear as we progress further into the text. In the process we hope that the reader will gain an appreciation of mathematics as an exacting, logical discipline.

In proving the following theorems on groups, it is essential to understand that we know nothing whatever about the actual nature of either the set $G$ or the operation $*$; both are completely abstract and unspecified. Our knowledge of $G$ and its associated operation is strictly confined to the information contained in the definition of group given earlier. The reader would be well-advised at this point to review Definition 2–10 on p. 21 before proceeding. We shall begin with a simple, yet highly important result.

**THEOREM 2–2.** The identity element of a group $(G, *)$ is unique, and each element of a group has precisely one inverse element.

*Proof.* Obviously any system which is a group is also a groupoid, so that Theorem 2–1 may be used to establish that the identity is unique. To show that an element has exactly one inverse in $G$, suppose the element $a \in G$ has two inverses, $a_1'$ and $a_2'$. Then according to the definition of inverse,

$$a * a_1' = a_1' * a = e, \qquad a * a_2' = a_2' * a = e.$$

But, identity element is the same in both cases (there is only one identity as we have just seen), so that

$$a * a_1' = a * a_2'.$$

Multiply both sides of this equation on the left by $a_1'$ (or by $a_2'$) to get

$$a_1' * (a * a_1') = a_1' * (a * a_2').$$

Using the associative law, we have $(a_1' * a) * a_1' = (a_1' * a) * a_2'$, and so

$$e * a_1' = e * a_2' \quad \text{or} \quad a_1' = a_2',$$

which means that $a$ has only one inverse.

An examination of the proof shows that we have actually established a little more than is indicated by the statement of the theorem. We have, in fact, also obtained a corollary:

> **COROLLARY.** Each element of a monoid has at most one inverse.

It is important to realize that two quite different types of uniqueness are involved in the above theorem. In the first case, the identity $e$ is the unique identity element for the entire set $G$. In the second, each element $a$ in $G$ has a unique inverse $a^{-1}$, which depends upon $a$; no "universal inverse" for all elements of $G$ is implied.

For the proof of the next theorem, we shall require a preliminary lemma.

> **LEMMA.** If $a, b, c, d \in G$ and $(G, *)$ is a semigroup, then
>
> $$(a * b) * (c * d) = a * ((b * c) * d).$$

*Proof.* Let us temporarily denote the product $c * d$ by $x$. Then, since the operation $*$ is associative, we have

$$\begin{aligned}
a * ((b * c) * d) &= a * (b * (c * d)) \\
&= a * (b * x) \\
&= (a * b) * x \\
&= (a * b) * (c * d).
\end{aligned}$$

> **THEOREM 2-3.** If $(G, *)$ is a group and $a, b \in G$, then
>
> $$(a * b)^{-1} = b^{-1} * a^{-1}.$$
>
> That is, the inverse of a product of group elements is the product of their inverses in reverse order.

*Proof.* According to the definition of inverse, all we need to show is that

$$(a * b) * (b^{-1} * a^{-1}) = (b^{-1} * a^{-1}) * (a * b) = e,$$

where $e$ is the group identity. From the uniqueness of the inverse of $a * b$, we would then conclude

$$(a * b)^{-1} = b^{-1} * a^{-1}.$$

Using the above lemma, we have

$$\begin{aligned}
(a * b) * (b^{-1} * a^{-1}) &= a * ((b * b^{-1}) * a^{-1}) \\
&= a * (e * a^{-1}) \\
&= a * a^{-1} \\
&= e.
\end{aligned}$$

A similar argument establishes that $(b^{-1} * a^{-1}) * (a * b) = e$.

EXAMPLE 2–24.  Let $G$ denote the set of all ordered pairs of real numbers with nonzero first components.  If the binary operation $*$ is defined on the set $G$ by the rule

$$(a, b) * (c, d) = (ac, bc + d),$$

then $(G, *)$ is a noncommutative group.  The identity element of the group is the pair $(1, 0)$; the inverse of an element $(a, b) \in G$ is $(1/a, -b/a)$.  A direct computation shows that

$$((1, 3) * (2, 4))^{-1} = (2, 10)^{-1} = (\tfrac{1}{2}, -5)$$

while,

$$(2, 4)^{-1} * (1, 3)^{-1} = (\tfrac{1}{2}, -2) * (1, -3) = (\tfrac{1}{2}, -5).$$

Thus $((1, 3) * (2, 4))^{-1} = (2, 4)^{-1} * (1, 3)^{-1}$, as is guaranteed by Theorem 2–3.  However, computing the product of the inverses in the order $(1, 3)^{-1} * (2, 4)^{-1}$, we obtain

$$(1, 3)^{-1} * (2, 4)^{-1} = (1, -3) * (\tfrac{1}{2}, -2) = (\tfrac{1}{2}, -\tfrac{7}{2})$$

so that

$$((1, 3) * (2, 4))^{-1} \neq (1, 3)^{-1} * (2, 4)^{-1}.$$

For this group then, the inverse of a product of elements is not equal to the product of their respective inverses in direct order.  This should not be particularly surprising inasmuch as the group $(G, *)$ is noncommutative.

**THEOREM 2–4 (Cancellation law).**  If $a$, $b$, and $c$ are elements of a group $(G, *)$ such that either

$$a * c = b * c \qquad \text{or} \qquad c * a = c * b,$$

then $a = b$.

*Proof.*  Since $c \in G$, $c^{-1}$ exists in $G$.  Multiplying the equation $a * c = b * c$ on the right side by $c^{-1}$, we obtain

$$(a * c) * c^{-1} = (b * c) * c^{-1}.$$

Then, by the associative law, this becomes

$$a * (c * c^{-1}) = b * (c * c^{-1})$$

or

$$a * e = b * e.$$

Hence $a = b$. Similarly, we can show that $c * a = c * b$ implies $a = b$.

This theorem allows us to cancel, from the same side, in equations in groups. We cannot conclude, however, that $a * c = c * b$ implies $a = b$, unless the group is known to be commutative.

An arbitrary binary operation need not satisfy the cancellation law. To see this, we consider the set $G = \{1, 2, 3\}$ under the following multiplication table:

| * | 1 | 2 | 3 |
|---|---|---|---|
| 1 | 1 | 2 | 3 |
| 2 | 2 | 1 | 2 |
| 3 | 3 | 2 | 1 |

By inspecting the table, we observe that $2 * 1 = 2 * 3$; but obviously $1 \neq 3$. The failure of the cancellation law in this instance results from the fact that when we multiply both sides of the equation $2 * 1 = 2 * 3$ by $2^{-1} = 2$, the element 2 does not associate with the product $2 * 3$; that is, $2 * (2 * 3) \neq (2 * 2) * 3$.

**THEOREM 2–5.** In a group $(G, *)$, the equation $a * x = b$ has a unique solution.

*Proof.* First, $x = a^{-1} * b$ satisfies the group equation $a * x = b$, since

$$a * (a^{-1} * b) = (a * a^{-1}) * b$$
$$= e * b$$
$$= b.$$

This shows that there is at least one solution in $G$; it remains for us to show that there is only one. Suppose there is some other element $y \in G$ such that $a * y = b$. Then

$$a * y = a * (a^{-1} * b),$$

so that by the cancellation law,

$$y = a^{-1} * b, \quad \text{or} \quad y = x.$$

**THEOREM 2–6.** If $(G, *)$ is a group, then the unique solution of the group equation $x * x = x$ is $x = e$.

*Proof.* Multiplying the equation $x * x = x$ on the left by $x^{-1}$ leads to

$$x^{-1} * (x * x) = x^{-1} * x.$$

Thus

$$x = e * x = (x^{-1} * x) * x = x^{-1} * (x * x) = x^{-1} * x = e.$$

An element $x \in S$ in a groupoid $(S, *)$ is said to be *idempotent* if $x * x = x$. Theorem 2–6 shows that a group possesses exactly one idempotent element, namely the group identity.

We shall conclude this section with two very important examples of groups; we shall have frequent occasion to refer to them.

EXAMPLE 2–25. The group to be introduced here is known as *the group of symmetries of a square.* Imagine a cardboard square having its sides parallel to the axes of a coordinate system and its center at the origin (Fig. 2–2):

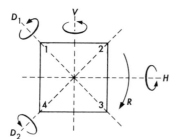

Figure 2–2

The elements of the set $G$ are taken to be certain rigid motions of the square. Permitted motions are the following: clockwise rotations $R_{90}$, $R_{180}$, $R_{270}$, and $R_{360}$ about the center through angles of 90, 180, 270, and 360 degrees, respectively; reflections (flips out of the plane and back into it) $H$ and $V$ about the horizontal and vertical lines through the center; reflections $D_1$ and $D_2$ about the indicated diagonals. We can "multiply" two such motions by performing them in succession, beginning with the one on the left. Thus $X * Y$ means the motion that achieves the same result as $X$ followed by $Y$.

For example, $H * R_{90}$ is that element of $G$ which has the same net effect as $H$ (a horizontal flip) followed by $R_{90}$ (a rotation clockwise through 90°). By observing the manner in which the numbered corners of the square are shifted around, we see that $H * R_{90}$ produces the same result as the single motion $D_1$; so $H * R_{90} = D_1$. A similar analysis shows $R_{90} * H = D_2$ from which we infer that our multiplication is not commutative.

The complete multiplication table for the operation $*$ is shown in Table 2–3.

TABLE 2–3

| $*$ | $R_{90}$ | $R_{180}$ | $R_{270}$ | $R_{360}$ | $H$ | $V$ | $D_1$ | $D_2$ |
|---|---|---|---|---|---|---|---|---|
| $R_{90}$ | $R_{180}$ | $R_{270}$ | $R_{360}$ | $R_{90}$ | $D_2$ | $D_1$ | $H$ | $V$ |
| $R_{180}$ | $R_{270}$ | $R_{360}$ | $R_{90}$ | $R_{180}$ | $V$ | $H$ | $D_2$ | $D_1$ |
| $R_{270}$ | $R_{360}$ | $R_{90}$ | $R_{180}$ | $R_{270}$ | $D_1$ | $D_2$ | $V$ | $H$ |
| $R_{360}$ | $R_{90}$ | $R_{180}$ | $R_{270}$ | $R_{360}$ | $H$ | $V$ | $D_1$ | $D_2$ |
| $H$ | $D_1$ | $V$ | $D_2$ | $H$ | $R_{360}$ | $R_{180}$ | $R_{90}$ | $R_{270}$ |
| $V$ | $D_2$ | $H$ | $D_1$ | $V$ | $R_{180}$ | $R_{360}$ | $R_{270}$ | $R_{90}$ |
| $D_1$ | $V$ | $D_2$ | $H$ | $D_1$ | $R_{270}$ | $R_{90}$ | $R_{360}$ | $R_{180}$ |
| $D_2$ | $H$ | $D_1$ | $V$ | $D_2$ | $R_{90}$ | $R_{270}$ | $R_{180}$ | $R_{360}$ |

Note that $R_{360}$ serves as the identity element and each of $R_{180}$, $R_{360}$, $H$, $V$, $D_1$, and $D_2$ is its own inverse, whereas $R_{90}$ and $R_{270}$ are inverses of each other. A direct verification establishes the associative law, thus making $(G, *)$ a group. Similar groups may be defined for other geometric figures (Problem 10 at the end of this section).

EXAMPLE 2–26.    Let $(G, *)$ be an arbitrary group. For a fixed element $a \in G$, define the *left-multiplication function* $f_a : G \to G$ by:

$$f_a(x) = a * x \qquad \text{for each} \qquad x \in G.$$

That is, $f_a$ multiplies (or *translates*) each element of $G$ by $a$ on the left. If $x \in G$, then

$$x = a * (a^{-1} * x) = f_a(a^{-1} * x),$$

so that $f_a$ maps $G$ onto itself. Moreover, $f_a$ is one-to-one, for if $x, y \in G$ with $f_a(x) = f_a(y)$, then $a * x = a * y$. From the cancellation law, we conclude that $x = y$.

Suppose we combine two of these mappings, say $f_a$ and $f_b$, under the usual composition of functions. For any $x \in G$, we see that

$$(f_a \circ f_b)(x) = f_a\big(f_b(x)\big) = f_a(b * x) = a * (b * x)$$
$$= (a * b) * x = f_{a*b}(x).$$

This means that $f_a \circ f_b = f_{a*b}$, so that the set of all such functions is closed under the operation of functional composition.

For the sake of notation, set $F_G = \{f_a \mid a \in G\}$. In view of the above argument, the system $(F_G, \circ)$ is a groupoid. Our aim is to show that it is actually a group.

Indeed, if $e$ is the identity element for $(G, *)$, then $f_e$ acts as the identity for $(F_G, \circ)$, since

$$f_a \circ f_e = f_{a*e} = f_a = f_{e*a} = f_e \circ f_a.$$

Moreover, $(f_a)^{-1} = f_{a^{-1}}$, for we have

$$f_a \circ f_{a^{-1}} = f_{a*a^{-1}} = f_e = f_{a^{-1}*a} = f_{a^{-1}} \circ f_a.$$

We already know that composition of functions is associative (Theorem 1–4), so it follows that $(F_G, \circ)$ is a group.

## PROBLEMS

1. Given that $a$, $b$, $c$, and $d$ are elements of the semigroup $(G, *)$, prove that

$$((a * b) * c) * d = a * (b * (c * d)).$$

2. Suppose $(G, *)$ is a group. Define a new binary operation $\circ$ on the set $G$ by the rule $a \circ b = b * a$. Show that $(G, \circ)$ is also a group, the so-called *opposite group* of $(G, *)$.

3. Given $(G_1, *)$ and $(G_2, *)$ are both groups, determine whether $(G_1 \cup G_2, *)$ is also a group.

4. Prove the theorem: A group $(G, *)$ is commutative if and only if $(a * b)^{-1} = a^{-1} * b^{-1}$ for every $a, b \in G$.

5. In any group $(G, *)$, the powers of an element $a \in G$ may be defined by

$$a^k = a * a * \cdots * a \qquad (k \text{ factors}),$$
$$a^0 = e, \qquad a^{-k} = (a^{-1})^k.$$

   where $k \in Z_+$. Establish the two usual laws of exponents, $a^k * a^j = a^{k+j}$, $(a^k)^j = a^{kj}$.

6. Given $a$ and $b$ are elements of a group $(G, *)$, with $a * b = b * a$, show that $(a * b)^k = a^k * b^k$.

7. Let $(G, *)$ be a group such that $(a * b)^2 = a^2 * b^2$ for every $a, b \in G$. Prove that the group is commutative.

8. Given $a^2 = e$ for every element $a$ of the group $(G, *)$, show that the group must be commutative.

9. A group $(G, *)$ is said to be *cyclic* if there exists an element $a \in G$ such that every element of $G$ is of the form $a^k$ for some integer $k$ (positive, negative, or zero). Such an element $a$ is called a *generator* of the group.

   (a) Prove that any cyclic group is commutative.
   (b) Given $G = \{1, -1, i, -i\}$, with $i^2 = -1$, show that $(G, \cdot)$ is a cyclic group. Which of its elements are generators?

10. Let the set $G$ consist of certain rigid motions of an equilateral triangle. Permitted motions are three clockwise rotations $R_{120}$, $R_{240}$, and $R_{360}$ about the center through angles of 120, 240, and 360 degrees, respectively, and three reflections $L_1$, $L_2$, and $L_3$ about lines $l_1$, $l_2$, and $l_3$ as indicated (Fig. 2–3). As usual, define the operation $*$ on $G$ to be one motion followed by another. Prove that the system $(G, *)$ is a group.

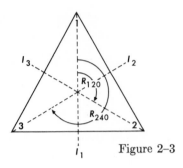

Figure 2–3

11. Let $(G, *)$ and $(H, \circ)$ be two distinct groups. Define a binary operation $\cdot$ on the Cartesian product

$$G \times H = \{(g, h) \mid g \in G, h \in H\}$$

as follows: for

$$(g_1, h_1), (g_2, h_2) \in G \times H,$$

set

$$(g_1, h_1) \cdot (g_2, h_2) = (g_1 * g_2, h_1 \circ h_2).$$

Prove that $(G \times H, \cdot)$ is a group; show further that this group is commutative whenever the original groups are commutative.

## 2–3.  THE GROUP OF INTEGERS MODULO $n$

We shall first investigate the notion of congruence, in terms of which the group of integers modulo $n$ will be formulated.

> **DEFINITION 2–11.**  Let $n$ be a fixed positive integer. Two integers $a$ and $b$ are said to be *congruent modulo $n$*, written
>
> $a \equiv b \pmod{n}$,
>
> if and only if the difference $a - b$ is divisible by $n$. That is, $a \equiv b \pmod{n}$ if and only if $a - b = kn$ for some integer $k$.

For instance, if $n = 7$, we have

$$3 \equiv 24 \pmod{7},$$
$$-5 \equiv 2 \pmod{7},$$
$$-8 \equiv -50 \pmod{7}, \text{ etc.}$$

Note that every pair of integers are congruent modulo 1, while a pair of integers are congruent modulo 2 provided they are both even or both odd.

Congruence is a kind of equality in the sense that it has many properties reminiscent of ordinary equality. Some of these properties are listed in the following theorem.

**THEOREM 2–7.** Let $n$ be a fixed positive integer and $a$, $b$, $c$ be arbitrary integers. Then

(1) $a \equiv a \pmod{n}$;

(2) if $a \equiv b \pmod{n}$, then $b \equiv a \pmod{n}$;

(3) if $a \equiv b \pmod{n}$ and $b \equiv c \pmod{n}$, then $a \equiv c \pmod{n}$;

(4) if $a \equiv b \pmod{n}$ and $c \equiv d \pmod{n}$, then
$$a + c \equiv b + d \pmod{n}, \qquad ac \equiv bd \pmod{n};$$

(5) if $a \equiv b \pmod{n}$, then $ac \equiv bc \pmod{n}$;

(6) if $a \equiv b \pmod{n}$, then $a^k \equiv b^k \pmod{n}$ for every positive integer $k$.

*Proof.* For any integer $a$, $a - a = 0n$, so that $a \equiv a \pmod{n}$ by Definition 2–11. If $a \equiv b \pmod{n}$, then $a - b = kn$ for some integer $k$. Hence $b - a = (-k)n$, where $-k$ is an integer. This yields (2).

To obtain (3), suppose that $a \equiv b \pmod{n}$ and $b \equiv c \pmod{n}$. Then $a - b = kn$ and $b - c = hn$ for some integers $k$, $h$. Therefore

$$a - c = (a - b) + (b - c) = kn + hn = (k + h)n,$$

which implies $a \equiv c \pmod{n}$.

Similarly, if $a \equiv b \pmod{n}$ and $c \equiv d \pmod{n}$, then there exist integers $k_1$, $k_2$ such that $a - b = k_1 n$ and $c - d = k_2 n$. Consequently,

$$(a + c) - (b + d) = (a - b) + (c - d) = k_1 n + k_2 n$$
$$= (k_1 + k_2)n$$

or

$$a + c \equiv b + d \pmod{n}.$$

Also,

$$ac = (b + k_1 n)(d + k_2 n) = bd + (bk_2 + dk_1 + k_1 k_2 n)n.$$

Since $bk_2 + dk_1 + k_1 k_2 n$ is an integer, $ac - bd$ is divisible by $n$, so that $ac \equiv bd \pmod{n}$. This establishes (4).

Property (5) follows directly from the second part of (4), since $c \equiv c \pmod{n}$.

Finally, we prove (6) by an inductive argument. The statement is certainly true for $k = 1$. Assuming it holds for an arbitrary $k$, we must show that it also holds for $k + 1$. But this is immediate from (4), since $a^k \equiv b^k \pmod{n}$ and $a \equiv b \pmod{n}$ imply $a^k a \equiv b^k b \pmod{n}$, or $a^{k+1} \equiv b^{k+1} \pmod{n}$.

**DEFINITION 2–12.** For a fixed integer $a$, let $[a]$ denote the set of all integers congruent to $a$ modulo $n$:

$$[a] = \{x \in Z \mid x \equiv a \pmod{n}\}$$
$$= \{x \in Z \mid x = a + kn \text{ for some integer } k\}.$$

We call $[a]$ the *congruence class, modulo $n$, determined by $a$*.

As an illustration, suppose that we are dealing with congruence modulo 3. Then

$$[0] = \{x \in Z \mid x = 3k \text{ for some } k \in Z\}$$
$$= \{\ldots, -9, -6, -3, 0, 3, 6, 9, \ldots\}.$$

Also,

$$[1] = \{x \in Z \mid x = 1 + 3k \text{ for some } k \in Z\}$$
$$= \{\ldots, -8, -5, -2, 1, 4, 7, 10, \ldots\}.$$

Similarly,

$$[2] = \{\ldots, -7, -4, -1, 2, 5, 8, 11, \ldots\}.$$

Observe that every integer lies in one of these three classes. Integers in the same congruence class are congruent modulo 3, while integers in different classes are not congruent modulo 3.

To return to the general case of congruence modulo $n$, let

$$Z_n = \{[0], [1], [2], \ldots, [n - 1]\}.$$

This particular collection of congruence classes is commonly referred to as the *integers modulo $n$*. It should be emphasized that the elements of $Z_n$ are not single integers but rather infinite sets of integers.

Several properties of the collection $Z_n$ which we shall require later are next established.

**THEOREM 2–8.** Let $n$ be a positive integer and $Z_n$ be the set of integers modulo $n$. Then

(1) for each $[a] \in Z_n$, $[a] \neq \emptyset$;

(2) if $[a] \in Z_n$ and $b \in [a]$, then $[b] = [a]$; that is, any element of the congruence class $[a]$ determines the class;

(3) for any $[a], [b] \in Z_n$ where $[a] \neq [b]$, $[a] \cap [b] = \emptyset$;

(4) $\cup_{[a] \in Z_n} [a] = Z$.

*Proof.* It is obvious that $a \in [a]$, since $a \equiv a \pmod{n}$. To prove (2), let $b \in [a]$ so that $b \equiv a \pmod{n}$. Suppose that $x \in [b]$, which implies $x \equiv b \pmod{n}$. By Theorem 2–7 (3), $x \equiv a \pmod{n}$, so that $x \in [a]$ also. This shows the inclusion $[b] \subseteq [a]$. A similar argument yields the opposite inclusion and consequently the equality $[a] = [b]$.

We obtain (3) by assuming to the contrary that some integer $c \in [a] \cap [b]$. Then by (2), which we have just established, $[a] = [c] = [b]$, which is an obvious contradiction.

Finally, since each class $[a] \subseteq Z$, the inclusion

$$\cup \{[a] \mid [a] \in Z_n\} \subseteq Z$$

is obvious. To obtain the reverse inclusion, we need only demonstrate that each integer belongs to some congruence class in $Z_n$. Let $x$ be any integer. If $x \neq 0$, then by the division algorithm, $x$ is uniquely expressible in the form $x = qn + r$, where $q, r \in Z$ and $0 \leq r \leq n - 1$. Thus $x - r = qn$ or $x \equiv r \pmod{n}$. This means that $x \in [r]$, where $[r]$ is an element of $Z_n$. On the other hand, if $x = 0$ then $x \in [0]$.

By a *partition* of $Z$, we mean a collection of nonempty subsets of $Z$ which are disjoint and whose union is $Z$. Theorem 2–8 shows that the integers modulo $n$ constitute a partition of $Z$ for each $n \in Z_+$.

**DEFINITION 2–13.** A binary operation $+_n$ may be defined on $Z_n$ as follows: for each $[a], [b] \in Z_n$, let $[a] +_n [b] = [a + b]$.

There is a minor problem involved in this definition. Inasmuch as the sum of two congruence classes in $Z_n$ is defined in terms of representatives from these classes, we must show that the operation $+_n$ does not depend on the two representatives chosen. More formally, it must be proven that if $[a'] = [a]$ and $[b'] = [b]$, then $[a' + b'] = [a + b]$. Now $a' \in [a'] = [a]$ and $b' \in [b'] = [b]$, which implies

$$a' \equiv a \pmod{n} \quad \text{and} \quad b' \equiv b \pmod{n}.$$

By virtue of Theorem 2–7 (4), it follows that

$$a' + b' \equiv a + b \pmod{n}$$

or $a' + b' \in [a + b]$. Theorem 2–8 (2) indicates that $[a' + b'] = [a + b]$, as desired.

As typical examples of modulo addition, we cite the following:

$$[3] +_7 [6] = [3 + 6] = [9] = [2],$$
$$[5] +_7 [2] = [5 + 2] = [7] = [0].$$

We are finally in a position to present the main result of this section.

**THEOREM 2–9.** For each positive integer $n$, the mathematical system $(Z_n, +_n)$ forms a commutative group, known as the *group of integers modulo* $n$.

*Proof.* The associativity and commutativity of the operation $+_n$ is a direct consequence of the same properties of the integers under ordinary addition. Indeed, if $[a], [b], [c] \in Z_n$, then

$$
\begin{aligned}
[a] +_n ([b] +_n [c]) &= [a] +_n [b + c] \\
&= [a + (b + c)] \\
&= [(a + b) + c] \\
&= [a + b] +_n [c] \\
&= ([a] +_n [b]) +_n [c].
\end{aligned}
$$

Similarly,

$$
[a] +_n [b] = [a + b] = [b + a] = [b] +_n [a].
$$

By definition of $+_n$, it is clear that $[0]$ is the identity element. Finally, if $[a] \in Z_n$, then $[n - a] \in Z_n$ and

$$
[a] +_n [n - a] = [a + (n - a)] = [n] = [0],
$$

so that $[a]^{-1} = [n - a]$.

For simplicity, it is convenient to remove the brackets in the designation of the congruence classes of $Z_n$. That is, we often write

$$
Z_n = \{0, 1, 2, \ldots, n - 1\}.
$$

With this notation, the operation table for, say $(Z_4, +_4)$, looks like the following.

| $+_4$ | 0 | 1 | 2 | 3 |
|-------|---|---|---|---|
| 0 | 0 | 1 | 2 | 3 |
| 1 | 1 | 2 | 3 | 0 |
| 2 | 2 | 3 | 0 | 1 |
| 3 | 3 | 0 | 1 | 2 |

## PROBLEMS

1. Write out the multiplication table for the group $(Z_6, +_6)$.

2. Prove that if $a \equiv b \pmod{n}$, then $ca \equiv cb \pmod{cn}$.

3. (a) Find all solutions $x$, where $0 \leq x < 15$, of the equation $3x \equiv 6 \pmod{15}$.
   (b) Prove that $6^n \equiv 6 \pmod{10}$ for any $n \in Z_+$.

4. Describe the partition of $Z$ determined by the integers modulo 5.

5. (a) Prove that if $ac \equiv bc \pmod{n}$, with $n$ a prime number, then $a \equiv b \pmod{n}$.
   (b) Show by example that $ac \equiv bc \pmod{n}$ does not always imply $a \equiv b \pmod{n}$.

6. Let $P(x)$ be a polynomial in $x$ with integral coefficients. If $a$ is a solution of the equation $P(x) \equiv 0$ (mod $n$), and $a \equiv b$ (mod $n$), prove that $b$ is also a solution.

7. Show that the pair $(\{0, 4, 8, 12\}, +_{16})$ is a group.

8. Use the fact that $10 \equiv 1$ (mod 9) to prove that an integer is divisible by 9 if and only if the sum of its digits is divisible by 9. [*Hint:* Express the integer in decimal form as a sum of powers of 10.]

9. For any integer $n$, prove that either $n^2 \equiv 0$ (mod 4) or $n^2 \equiv 1$ (mod 4).

## 2–4. SUBGROUPS AND COSETS

From various examples and exercises, the reader may have noticed that certain subsets of the elements of a group lead to new groups when one restricts the group operation to these subsets. Indeed, this situation occurs quite frequently and will be the object of our investigation in the present section.

> **DEFINITION 2–14.** Let $(G, *)$ be a group and $H \subseteq G$ be a nonempty subset of $G$. The pair $(H, *)$ is said to be a *subgroup* of $(G, *)$ if $(H, *)$ is itself a group, using the same operation $*$ of $(G, *)$.

Each group $(G, *)$ has two obvious subgroups. For, if $e \in G$ is the identity element of the group $(G, *)$, then both $(\{e\}, *)$ and $(G, *)$ are subgroups of $(G, *)$. These two subgroups are often referred to as the *improper* or *trivial* subgroups of $(G, *)$; all subgroups between these two extremes are called *nontrivial* subgroups.

EXAMPLE 2–27. If $Z_e$ and $Z_o$ denote the sets of even and odd integers, respectively, then $(Z_e, +)$ is a subgroup of the group $(Z, +)$, while $(Z_o, +)$ is not.

EXAMPLE 2–28. Consider $(Z_6, +_6)$, the group of integers modulo 6. If $H = \{0, 2, 4\}$, then $(H, +_6)$, whose operation table is given below, is a subgroup of $(Z_6, +_6)$.

| $+_6$ | 0 | 2 | 4 |
|-------|---|---|---|
| 0     | 0 | 2 | 4 |
| 2     | 2 | 4 | 0 |
| 4     | 4 | 0 | 2 |

EXAMPLE 2–29. Let $(G, *)$ be the group of symmetries of the square (see Example 2–25), where $G = \{R_{90}, R_{180}, R_{270}, R_{360}, H, V, D_1, D_2\}$ and the operation $*$ consists of following one motion by another. This group contains eight nontrivial subgroups. We leave it to the reader to verify

that the following sets comprise the elements of these subgroups:

$$\{R_{90}, R_{180}, R_{270}, R_{360}\}, \quad \{R_{180}, R_{360}, H, V\},$$
$$\{R_{180}, R_{360}, D_1, D_2\}, \quad \{R_{180}, R_{360}\}, \quad \{R_{360}, D_1\},$$
$$\{R_{360}, D_2\}, \quad \{R_{360}, H\}, \quad \{R_{360}, V\}.$$

Suppose $(H, *)$ is a subgroup of the group $(G, *)$. Since the identity element of $(H, *)$ satisfies the equation $x * x = x$, it must be the same as the identity of the larger group $(G, *)$, for otherwise we would have two idempotent elements in $G$, contrary to Theorem 2–6. The identity element of a group then also serves as the identity element for any of its subgroups. Moreover, the uniqueness of the inverse elements in a group implies the inverse of $h \in H$ in the subgroup $(H, *)$ is the same as its inverse in the whole group $(G, *)$.

To establish that a given subset $H$ of $G$, along with the induced operation of $(G, *)$, constitutes a subgroup, we must verify that all the conditions of Definition 2–10 are satisfied. However, the associativity of the operation $*$ in $H$ is an immediate consequence of its associativity in $G$, since $H \subseteq G$. It is necessary then to show only the following:

(1) $a, b \in H$ implies $a * b \in H$   (closure);
(2) $e \in H$, where $e$ is the identity element of $(G, *)$;
(3) $a \in H$ implies $a^{-1} \in H$.

A theorem which establishes a single convenient criterion for determining subgroups is given below:

**THEOREM 2–10.** Let $(G, *)$ be a group and $\emptyset \neq H \subseteq G$. Then $(H, *)$ is a subgroup of $(G, *)$ if and only if $a, b \in H$ implies $a * b^{-1} \in H$.

*Proof.* If $(H, *)$ is a subgroup and $a, b \in H$, then $b^{-1} \in H$, and so $a * b^{-1} \in H$ by the closure axiom. Conversely, suppose $H$ is a nonempty subset of $G$ which contains the element $a * b^{-1}$ whenever $a, b \in H$. Since $H$ contains some element $a$, $a * a^{-1} = e \in H$, applying the hypothesis to the pair $a, a \in H$. Then $e * b^{-1} = b^{-1} \in H$ for every $b \in H$. Finally, if $a$ and $b$ are in $H$, using the pair $a, b^{-1} \in H$, we obtain $a * (b^{-1})^{-1} = a * b \in H$. As we remarked before, the set $H$ "inherits" the associative law as a subset of $G$, so that all the group axioms are satisfied, and $(H, *)$ is therefore a subgroup of $(G, *)$.

**DEFINITION 2–15.** The *center* of a group $(G, *)$, denoted by cent $G$, is the set

cent $G = \{c \in G \mid c * x = x * c \text{ for all } x \in G\}.$

Thus cent $G$ consists of those elements which commute with every element of $G$. For example, in the group of symmetries of the square, cent $G = \{R_{180}, R_{360}\}$. The reader may already have deduced that a group $(G, *)$ is commutative if and only if cent $G = G$.

As illustrations of the use of Theorem 2–10 in determining when a subset of the elements of a group is the set of elements of a subgroup, we present the following two theorems.

> **THEOREM 2–11.** The pair (cent $G$, $*$) is a subgroup of each group $(G, *)$.

*Proof.* We first observe that cent $G$ is nonempty, for in particular $e \in$ cent $G$. Now consider any two elements $a, b \in$ cent $G$. By the definition of center, we know that $a * x = x * a$ and $b * x = x * b$ for every element $x$ of $G$. Thus, if $x \in G$

$$
\begin{aligned}
(a * b^{-1}) * x &= a * (b^{-1} * x) \\
&= a * (x^{-1} * b)^{-1} \\
&= a * (b * x^{-1})^{-1} \\
&= a * (x * b^{-1}) \\
&= (a * x) * b^{-1} \\
&= (x * a) * b^{-1} = x * (a * b^{-1}),
\end{aligned}
$$

which implies $a * b^{-1} \in$ cent $G$. According to Theorem 2–10, this is a sufficient condition for (cent $G$, $*$) to be a subgroup of $(G, *)$.

> **THEOREM 2–12.** If $(G_1, *)$ and $(G_2, *)$ are both subgroups of the group $(G, *)$, then $(G_1 \cap G_2, *)$ is also a subgroup.

*Proof.* The set $G_1 \cap G_2 \neq \emptyset$, since $e \in G_1 \cap G_2$. Suppose that $a, b \in G_1 \cap G_2$. Then $a, b \in G_1$ and $a, b \in G_2$. Since $(G_1, *)$ and $(G_2, *)$ are subgroups, Theorem 2–10 asserts that $a * b^{-1} \in G_1$ and $a * b^{-1} \in G_2$. That is, $a * b^{-1} \in G_1 \cap G_2$, which then implies $(G_1 \cap G_2, *)$ is a subgroup of $(G, *)$.

In the case of the symmetries of the square, we could take

$$G_1 = \{R_{90}, R_{180}, R_{270}, R_{360}\}$$

and

$$G_2 = \{R_{180}, R_{360}, H, V\}.$$

It was observed in Example 2–29 that $(G_1 \cap G_2, *) = (\{R_{180}, R_{360}\}, *)$ constitutes a subgroup of this group.

As we shall now see, each subgroup induces a decomposition of the elements of the group into disjoint subsets known as "cosets."

> **DEFINITION 2–16.** Let $(H, *)$ be a subgroup of the group $(G, *)$ and let $a \in G$. The set
>
> $$a * H = \{a * h \mid h \in H\}$$
>
> is called a *left coset* of $H$ in $G$. The element $a$ is *representative* of $a * H$.

In a similar fashion, we can define the right cosets $H * a$ of $H$. The right cosets of the same subgroup are in general different from the left cosets. If the group operation $*$ of $(G, *)$ is commutative, then clearly $a * H = H * a$ for all $a \in G$. In the subsequent discussions, we will generally consider only left cosets of a subgroup. It is obvious that a parallel theory for right cosets may be developed.

Before proceeding to an example, we shall make several simple observations. First, if $e$ is the identity element of $(G, *)$, then

$$e * H = \{e * h \mid h \in H\} = \{h \mid h \in H\} = H,$$

so that $H$ itself is a left coset of $H$. Moreover, since $e \in H$, we have

$$a = a * e \in a * H;$$

that is, every element $a$ of $G$ belongs to some left coset of $H$, and more specifically, to the coset $a * H$. We shall make use of this fact in a little while.

We note further that there is a one-to-one correspondence between the elements of $H$ and those of any coset of $H$. Indeed, if $a * H$ is a left coset of $H$, we may define a mapping $f \colon H \to a * H$ by $f(h) = a * h$. This function is onto $a * H$, since every element of $a * H$ is of the form $a * h$ for some choice of $h \in H$. In addition, $f$ is a one-to-one function, for if $a * h_1 = a * h_2$, where $h_1, h_2 \in H$, the cancellation law for groups yields $h_1 = h_2$. That is, $f(h_1) = f(h_2)$ implies $h_1 = h_2$. If the group $(G, *)$ has a finite number of elements, we may conclude that any two left cosets of $H$ have the same number of elements, namely, the number of elements in $H$.

EXAMPLE 2–30. Returning once again to the group of symmetries of the square, let us select the subgroup $(S, *)$, where $S = \{R_{360}, V\}$. The task of computing the left cosets of $S$ is straightforward, since we have an operation table for the group (see Example 2–25):

$$R_{90} * S = \{R_{90} * R_{360}, R_{90} * V\} = \{R_{90}, D_1\},$$
$$R_{180} * S = \{R_{180} * R_{360}, R_{180} * V\} = \{R_{180}, H\},$$
$$R_{270} * S = \{R_{270} * R_{360}, R_{270} * V\} = \{R_{270}, D_2\},$$
$$R_{360} * S = \{R_{360} * R_{360}, R_{360} * V\} = \{R_{360}, V\},$$
$$H * S = \{H * R_{360}, H * V\} = \{H, R_{180}\},$$
$$V * S = \{V * R_{360}, V * V\} = \{V, R_{360}\},$$
$$D_1 * S = \{D_1 * R_{360}, D_1 * V\} = \{D_1, R_{90}\},$$
$$D_2 * S = \{D_2 * R_{360}, D_2 * V\} = \{D_2, R_{270}\}.$$

From a quick inspection, the reader will observe that there are only four distinct cosets: $\{R_{90}, D_1\}$, $\{R_{180}, H\}$, $\{R_{270}, D_2\}$, and $\{R_{360}, V\} = S$. These cosets are disjoint and their union is the underlying set of elements of the whole group. As we shall see, this is always the case. Also, for this subgroup the notions of left and right cosets do not agree, since

$$D_1 * S = \{D_1, R_{90}\} \neq \{D_1, R_{270}\} = S * D_1.$$

**THEOREM 2–13.** If $(H, *)$ is a subgroup of the group $(G, *)$, then $a * H = H$ if and only if $a \in H$.

*Proof.* Suppose first that $a * H = H$. As we have just remarked, the fact that the identity $e$ is a member of $H$ implies that the element $a$ belongs to $a * H$, and thus by hypothesis to $H$ also. On the other hand, if $a \in H$, then $a * H \subseteq H$, since the set $H$, being the set of elements of a subgroup, is closed under the group operation $*$. The opposite inclusion is obtained by noting that each element $h \in H$ may be written as

$$h = a * (a^{-1} * h).$$

Here, $a^{-1} * h \in H$, since both $a, h \in H$ and $(H, *)$ is a subgroup of $(G, *)$. This implies that $h \in a * H$ and consequently $H \subseteq a * H$.

Our next theorem provides a simple criterion for the equality of two left cosets.

**THEOREM 2–14.** If $(H, *)$ is a subgroup of the group $(G, *)$, then

$$a * H = b * H$$

if and only if $a^{-1} * b \in H$.

*Proof.* Assume that $a * H = b * H$. Then, if $a * h_1$ is an arbitrary element of $a * H$, there must exist an $h_2 \in H$ such that $a * h_1 = b * h_2$. From this we conclude that

$$a^{-1} * b = h_1 * h_2^{-1}$$

and, since the product $h_1 * h_2^{-1}$ belongs to $H$, that $a^{-1} * b \in H$.

Conversely, if $a^{-1} * b \in H$, then by Theorem 2–13 we have

$$(a^{-1} * b) * H = H.$$

This implies that any element $h_1 \in H$ can be expressed as

$$h_1 = (a^{-1} * b) * h_2$$

for some $h_2 \in H$, from which we infer that

$$a * h_1 = b * h_2.$$

Thus each product $a * h_1$ in the coset $a * H$ is equal to an element of the form $b * h_2$, and consequently lies in the coset $b * H$. Since the converse also holds,

$$a * H = b * H.$$

As an immediate consequence of the above theorem, we see that any element $a_1$ of the left coset $a * H$ determines that coset. For if $a_1 \in a * H$, then $a_1 = a * h_1$ for suitable $h_1 \in H$. Thus $a^{-1} * a_1 \in H$, so that by the theorem, $a * H = a_1 * H$. This means that each element of a coset can be thought of as a representative of that coset.

We are now in a position to prove a fundamental result concerning cosets to the effect that if two left cosets have an element in common, then they are precisely the same set.

**THEOREM 2–15.** If $(H, *)$ is a subgroup of the group $(G, *)$, then either the cosets $a * H$ and $b * H$ are disjoint or otherwise $a * H = b * H$.

*Proof.* Suppose that $a * H$ and $b * H$ contain some element $c$ in common. Since $c$ is in $a * H$, there exists an $h_1 \in H$ such that $c = a * h_1$. Similarly,

$$c = b * h_2$$

for some element $h_2 \in H$. It follows then that

$$a * h_1 = b * h_2 \quad \text{or} \quad a^{-1} * b = h_1 * h_2^{-1}.$$

The product $h_1 * h_2^{-1}$ is in the set $H$, so that we conclude from Theorem 2–14 that

$$a * H = b * H.$$

We saw earlier that each element $a \in G$ is a member of some left coset of $H$ in $G$, namely, the coset $a * H$; that is, $G$ is exhausted by its left cosets. Theorem 2–15 indicates that an element can belong to one and only one left coset of $H$. Thus the set $G$ is partitioned by $H$ into disjoint sets, each of which has exactly as many elements as $H$.

EXAMPLE 2–31. Let $(Z, +)$ be the group of integers under addition. If the set $H$ consists of all integral multiples of 4,

$$H = \{4k \mid k \in Z\} = \{\ldots, -8, -4, 0, 4, 8, \ldots\},$$

then $(H, +)$ is a subgroup of $(Z, +)$. The distinct left cosets of $H$ in $Z$ are:

$$0 + H = \{\ldots, -8, -4, 0, 4, 8, \ldots\} = [0],$$
$$1 + H = \{\ldots, -7, -3, 1, 5, 9, \ldots\} = [1],$$
$$2 + H = \{\ldots, -6, -2, 2, 6, 10, \ldots\} = [2],$$
$$3 + H = \{\ldots, -5, -1, 3, 7, 11, \ldots\} = [3].$$

In other words, the left cosets of $H$ are just the four congruence classes of the integers modulo 4. In this case, the coset decomposition of $Z$ relative to $H$ is

$$Z = [0] \cup [1] \cup [2] \cup [3].$$

A group $(G, *)$ is termed *finite* if the underlying set $G$ consists of only a finite number of elements, and that number is called the *order* of $G$. Suppose that $(G, *)$ is a finite group, say, of order $n$, and $(H, *)$ is a subgroup of $(G, *)$ of order $r$. We can then decompose the set $G$ into a union of a finite number of disjoint left cosets of $H$:

$$G = (a_1 * H) \cup (a_2 * H) \cup \cdots \cup (a_k * H).$$

The number $k$ of distinct left cosets in this decomposition is called the *index* of $H$ in $G$. Since each coset appearing in the above decomposition has $r$ elements, $G$ itself has $r \cdot k$ elements, or $n = r \cdot k$. This establishes the following classical theorem due to Lagrange.

**THEOREM 2–16 (Lagrange).** The order of any subgroup of a finite group divides the order of the group.

From this, we are able to conclude that any finite group of prime order has no proper subgroups.

We next introduce a very important class of subgroups which we shall refer to as distinguished subgroups.

> **DEFINITION 2–17.** A subgroup $(H, *)$ of the group $(G, *)$ is said to be *distinguished* (or *normal*) in $(G, *)$ if and only if every left coset of $H$ in $G$ is also a right coset of $H$ in $G$.

Thus, if $(H, *)$ is distinguished and $a * H$ is any left coset of $H$ in $G$, there exists some element $b \in G$ such that

$$a * H = H * b.$$

Since $a$ is in the left coset $a * H$, this means that $a$ is also a member of the right coset $H * b$. The cosets $H * b$ and $H * a$ have the element $a$ in common; so the analogue of Theorem 2–15 for right cosets implies that

$$H * b = H * a.$$

In other words, if $a * H$ happens to be a right coset of $H$, then it must be the right coset $H * a$. This observation allows us to reformulate Definition 2–17 as follows.

> **DEFINITION 2–18.** A subgroup $(H, *)$ is distinguished in the group $(G, *)$ if and only if $a * H = H * a$ for every $a \in G$.

For a distinguished subgroup $(H, *)$, we may thus speak simply of the cosets of $H$ in $G$ without specifying right or left. The trivial subgroups are obviously distinguished. More generally, every subgroup of a commutative group is a distinguished subgroup.

Definition 2–18 indicates that distinguishability guarantees a weak form of commutativity relative to $H$. For, if $h \in H$, while we cannot in general conclude that $a * h = h * a$ for any $a \in G$, we do know that there exists a pair of elements $h_1, h_2 \in H$ such that

$$a * h_1 = h_2 * a.$$

The following theorem gives a convenient procedure for determining whether or not a given subgroup is indeed a distinguished subgroup, and we shall have several occasions to make use of it.

> **THEOREM 2–17.** The subgroup $(H, *)$ is a distinguished subgroup of the group $(G, *)$ if and only if for each element $a \in G$
>
> $$a * H * a^{-1} \subseteq H.$$

*Proof.* First, assume that $a * H * a^{-1} \subseteq H$ for any $a \in G$. We must prove that in this case $a * H = H * a$. Let $a * h$ be an arbitrary element of $a * H$. Since $a * H * a^{-1} \subseteq H$, $a * h * a^{-1} = h_1$ for some $h_1 \in H$. Thus

$$a * h = (a * h * a^{-1}) * a = h_1 * a.$$

The product $h_1 * a$ lies in the right coset $H * a$; so we conclude that

$$a * H \subseteq H * a.$$

We obtain the opposite inclusion, $H * a \subseteq a * H$, by a similar argument upon observing that our hypothesis also implies

$$a^{-1} * H * a = a^{-1} * H * (a^{-1})^{-1} \subseteq H.$$

Conversely, suppose $a * H = H * a$ for each $a \in G$. Let $a * h_1 * a^{-1}$ be any element in $a * H * a^{-1}$. Then, since $a * H = H * a$, there exists an element $h_2 \in H$ such that

$$a * h_1 = h_2 * a.$$

Consequently,

$$a * h_1 * a^{-1} = (h_2 * a) * a^{-1} = h_2,$$

which implies $a * H * a^{-1} \subseteq H$.

EXAMPLE 2–32. We shall make use of the theorem just proved to show that (cent $G$, $*$) is a distinguished subgroup of each group $(G, *)$. In terms of elements, we must prove that if $c \in$ cent $G$ and $a$ is arbitrary in $G$, then $a * c * a^{-1} \in$ cent $G$. But this is fairly obvious, since from the definition of cent $G$, $a * c = c * a$. It follows at once that

$$a * c * a^{-1} = c * a * a^{-1} = c \in \text{cent } G.$$

The significance of distinguished subgroups—indeed, our main purpose for introducing them—is that they enable us to define new groups which are associated in a natural way with the original group. More specifically, we will show that the set of cosets of a distinguished subgroup is itself the set of elements of a group.

If $(H, *)$ is a distinguished subgroup of the group $(G, *)$, then we shall denote the collection of distinct cosets of $H$ in $G$ by $G/H$:

$$G/H = \{a * H \mid a \in G\}.$$

These are also right cosets, for every $a * H = H * a$.

A rule of combination $\otimes$ may be defined on $G/H$ by the formula

$$(a * H) \otimes (b * H) = (a * b) * H.$$

Since this definition is stated in terms of coset representatives, we must first show that the multiplication of cosets under $\otimes$ is independent of the particular representatives which are chosen from these sets. That is, we must show that if

$$a * H = a_1 * H \qquad \text{and} \qquad b * H = b_1 * H,$$

then also

$$(a * b) * H = (a_1 * b_1) * H.$$

According to Theorem 2–14, it is sufficient merely to prove that the product

$$(a * b)^{-1} * (a_1 * b_1)$$

is a member of $H$. Now, $a * H = a_1 * H$ and $b * H = b_1 * H$ imply both $a^{-1} * a_1$, $b^{-1} * b_1 \in H$. Since $(H, *)$ is distinguished in $(G, *)$, we know that $x * H * x^{-1} \subseteq H$ for every $x \in G$. In particular,

$$b^{-1} * H * b = b^{-1} * H * (b^{-1})^{-1} \in H.$$

From this we conclude that $b^{-1} * (a^{-1} * a_1) * b \in H$ and thus

$$(a * b)^{-1} * (a_1 * b_1) = (b^{-1} * (a^{-1} * a_1) * b) * (b^{-1} * b_1) \in H.$$

As remarked above, this shows that $\otimes$ is a *well-defined* binary operation on $G/H$ in the sense that the product of two cosets depends only on the cosets involved and in no way on the representative elements chosen from them.

**THEOREM 2–18.** If $(H, *)$ is a distinguished subgroup of the group $(G, *)$, then the system $(G/H, \otimes)$ forms a group, known as the *quotient group* of $G$ by $H$.

*Proof.* First, let us observe that the associativity of the operation $\otimes$ is a direct consequence of the associativity of $*$ in $G$:

$$
\begin{aligned}
[(a * H) \otimes (b * H)] \otimes (c * H) \\
= ((a * b) * H) \otimes (c * H) \\
= ((a * b) * c) * H \\
= (a * (b * c)) * H \\
= (a * H) \otimes ((b * c) * H) \\
= (a * H) \otimes [(b * H) \otimes (c * H)].
\end{aligned}
$$

The coset $H = e * H$ is the identity element for the operation $\otimes$, since

$$
\begin{aligned}
(a * H) \otimes (e * H) &= (a * e) * H = a * H \\
&= (e * a) * H \\
&= (e * H) \otimes (a * H).
\end{aligned}
$$

It is also easy to see from the definition of $\otimes$ that the inverse of the coset $a * H$ is $a^{-1} * H \in G/H$, where $a^{-1}$ denotes the inverse of $a$ in $G$. Thus all the group postulates are fulfilled.

We close this section with an example from a group we have used before.

EXAMPLE 2–33. In the group of symmetries of the square, the subgroup

$$
(S, *) = (\{R_{180}, R_{360}\}, *)
$$

is distinguished, being the center of the group. Its distinct cosets—that is, the elements of $G/S$— are:

$$
G/S = \big\{ \{R_{180}, R_{360}\}, \quad \{R_{90}, R_{270}\}, \quad \{V, H\}, \quad \{D_1, D_2\} \big\}.
$$

A typical coset multiplication proceeds as follows:

$$
\begin{aligned}
\{D_1, D_2\} \otimes \{R_{90}, R_{270}\} &= (D_1 * S) \otimes (R_{90} * S) \\
&= (D_1 * R_{90}) * S \\
&= V * S \\
&= \{V, H\}.
\end{aligned}
$$

To multiply two cosets under $\otimes$, all we really need to do is select an arbitrary representative from each coset, multiply these elements under the group operation $*$ and determine to which coset the resulting product belongs.

TABLE 2–4

| $\otimes$ | $\{R_{180}, R_{360}\}$ | $\{R_{90}, R_{270}\}$ | $\{V, H\}$ | $\{D_1, D_2\}$ |
|---|---|---|---|---|
| $\{R_{180}, R_{360}\}$ | $\{R_{180}, R_{360}\}$ | $\{R_{90}, R_{270}\}$ | $\{V, H\}$ | $\{D_1, D_2\}$ |
| $\{R_{90}, R_{270}\}$ | $\{R_{90}, R_{270}\}$ | $\{R_{180}, R_{360}\}$ | $\{D_1, D_2\}$ | $\{V, H\}$ |
| $\{V, H\}$ | $\{V, H\}$ | $\{D_1, D_2\}$ | $\{R_{180}, R_{360}\}$ | $\{R_{90}, R_{270}\}$ |
| $\{D_1, D_2\}$ | $\{D_1, D_2\}$ | $\{V, H\}$ | $\{R_{90}, R_{270}\}$ | $\{R_{180}, R_{360}\}$ |

The operation table for the quotient group $(G/S, \otimes)$ is shown in Table 2–4.

## PROBLEMS

1. In each of the following cases, establish that $(H, \cdot)$ is a subgroup of the group $(G, \cdot)$:
   (a) $H = \{1, -1\}$, $G = \{1, -1, i, -i\}$, where $i^2 = -1$
   (b) $H = \{2^n \mid n \in Z\}$, $G = Q - \{0\}$
   (c) $H = Z - \{0\}$, $G = Q - \{0\}$

2. Prove that $(\{0, 3, 6, 9\}, +_{12})$ is a subgroup of $(Z_{12}, +_{12})$, the group of integers modulo 12.

3. Show by example that if $(H_1, *)$ and $(H_2, *)$ are both subgroups of the group $(G, *)$, then $(H_1 \cup H_2, *)$ is not necessarily a subgroup.

4. Prove that if $(H, *)$ is a subgroup of the group $(G, *)$ and $(K, *)$ is a subgroup of $(H, *)$, then $(K, *)$ is also a subgroup of $(G, *)$.

5. Let $(H, *)$ be a subgroup of the group $(G, *)$. We say that two elements $a$ and $b$ of $G$ are *congruent modulo $H$*, written $a \equiv b \pmod{H}$, if and only if $a * b^{-1} \in H$. Establish that if $a, b, c \in G$, then:
   (a) $a \equiv a \pmod{H}$
   (b) $a \equiv b \pmod{H}$ implies $b \equiv a \pmod{H}$
   (c) $a \equiv b \pmod{H}$ and $b \equiv c \pmod{H}$ implies $a \equiv c \pmod{H}$

6. Suppose that $(G, *)$ is a group and $a \in G$.
   (a) Let $H_a$ denote the set of all integral powers of $a$:
   $$H_a = \{a^k \mid k \in Z\}.$$
   Prove that the pair $(H_a, *)$ is a commutative subgroup of $(G, *)$, known as the *cyclic subgroup generated by $a$*. This shows that each element of $G$ belongs to at least one subgroup.
   (b) Let $N_a$ denote the set of all elements of $G$ which commute with $a$:
   $$N_a = \{x \in G \mid a * x = x * a\}.$$
   Prove that the pair $(N_a, *)$ is a subgroup of $(G, *)$, known as the *centralizer* of $a$ in $G$. Also verify the equality: cent $G = \bigcap_{a \in G} N_a$.

7. Given $(G, *)$ is a finite group, prove that:
   (a) For each element $a \in G$ there exists a positive integer $k$ such that $a^k = e$.
   (b) If $H$ is a nonempty subset of $G$ which is closed under the operation $*$, then $(H, *)$ is a subgroup of $(G, *)$.
   (c) If $(G, *)$ is of prime order, then it is cyclic.

8. In the group $(G, *)$, define the set $H$ by
   $$H = \{a \in G \mid a^k = e \text{ for some } k \in Z_+\}.$$
   Determine if the pair $(H, *)$ is a subgroup of $(G, *)$.

9. Assume $(H, *)$ is an arbitrary subgroup of the group $(G, *)$.
   (a) Show by example that the product of two left cosets of $H$ in $G$ need not be well defined.

(b) Prove that $(c * a) * H = (c * b) * H$ implies $a * H = b * H$.

(c) Show that there exists a one-to-one correspondence between the left cosets of $H$ in $G$ and the right cosets of $H$ in $G$.

10. Determine the left coset decomposition of the group of symmetries of the square with respect to the subgroup $(\{R_{360}, D_1\}, *)$.

11. In the group of symmetries of the equilateral triangle, find:

(a) all subgroups,
(b) all distinguished subgroups,
(c) the center of the group.

12. Given $(H_1, *)$ and $(H_2, *)$ are both subgroups of the group $(G, *)$ and one of these subgroups is distinguished, prove that $(H_1 \cap H_2, *)$ is a distinguished subgroup of $(G, *)$.

13. Let $(H, *)$ be a subgroup of the group $(G, *)$ and the set $N_H$ be defined by:

$$N_H = \{a \in G \mid a * H * a^{-1} \subseteq H\}.$$

(a) Prove that the pair $(N_H, *)$ is a subgroup of $(G, *)$, called the *normalizer* of $H$ in $G$.

(b) Prove that $(N_H, *)$ is distinguished if and only if $N_H = G$.

14. Suppose that $(H, *)$ and $(K, *)$ are distinguished subgroups of the group $(G, *)$, with $H \cap K = \{e\}$. By considering elements of the form $h * k * h^{-1} * k^{-1}$, show that $h * k = k * h$ for all $h \in H$, $k \in K$.

15. Describe the quotient group of:

(a) $(Z_e, +)$ in $(Z, +)$          (b) $(\{0, 2, 4, 6, 8\}, +_{10})$ in $(Z_{10}, +_{10})$

(c) $(Z, +)$ in $(Q, +)$          (d) $(\{1, -1\}, \cdot)$ in $(\{1, -1, i, -i\}, \cdot)$

16. Given $(H, *)$ is a distinguished subgroup of the group $(G, *)$, prove that the quotient group $(G/H, \otimes)$ is commutative provided that $(G, *)$ is commutative.

## 2-5. OPERATION-PRESERVING FUNCTIONS

In this section we shall introduce a concept which will be of fundamental importance throughout the remainder of the book and is in fact one of the most important notions in mathematics: the idea of algebraically indistinguishable systems. First, we shall define and investigate a class of functions which preserve algebraic structure.

**DEFINITION 2-19.** Let $(G, *)$ be a group and $f$ a function which maps the set $G$ into itself, $f: G \to G$. Then $f$ is said to be an *operation-preserving function* (or *homomorphism*) *from* $(G, *)$ *into itself* if and only if

$$f(a * b) = f(a) * f(b)$$

for every pair of elements $a, b \in G$.

The mappings indicated in this definition have the property of preserving products in $G$. A common way of phrasing this is to say that the image of a product under $f$ equals the product of the images. A function $f$ is operation-preserving if the two procedures described by the following diagram yield the same result in $G$.

$$
\begin{array}{ccc}
(a, b) & \xrightarrow{\quad * \quad} & a * b \\
\downarrow{\scriptstyle f} & & \downarrow \\
(f(a), f(b)) & \xrightarrow{\quad * \quad} & f(a * b) = f(a) * f(b)
\end{array}
$$

In other words, it is immaterial whether we first form the product $a * b$ and then apply $f$ to it, or first obtain the images $f(a)$ and $f(b)$ and then take their product; the operations $f$ and $*$ are, in a sense, interchangeable.

EXAMPLE 2–34. Let $(G, *)$ be an arbitrary group. Define the function $f: G \to G$ by $f(a) = a$. Then

$$f(a * b) = a * b = f(a) * f(b),$$

so that $f$ is operation-preserving.

EXAMPLE 2–35. Let $(Z, +)$ be the group of integers under addition. For the integer $n \in Z$, define $f$ by $f(n) = 2n$. In order to verify that this mapping is operation-preserving, we must check to see whether $f(a + b) = f(a) + f(b)$. One can easily verify this, for

$$f(a + b) = 2(a + b) = 2a + 2b = f(a) + f(b).$$

EXAMPLE 2–36. Again let $(Z, +)$ be the group, but now define the function $f: Z \to Z$ by $f(a) = a + 1$. That $f$ is not operation-preserving follows from

$$f(a + b) = a + b + 1 \neq (a + 1) + (b + 1) = f(a) + f(b).$$

The requirement in Definition 2–19 that the function $f$ map the group into itself is unnecessarily restrictive. It would be more natural to consider mappings from one group into another. This prompts the following definition.

**DEFINITION 2-20.** Let $(G_1, *)$ and $(G_2, \circ)$ be two groups and $f$ a function from $G_1$ into $G_2$, $f: G_1 \to G_2$. Then $f$ is said to be an *operation-preserving function* (or *homomorphism*) *from* $(G_1, *)$ *into* $(G_2, \circ)$ if and only if

$$f(a * b) = f(a) \circ f(b)$$

for every pair of elements $a, b \in G_1$.

Observe that on the left side of the above equation, the product $a * b$ is computed in $G_1$, while on the right side the product $f(a) \circ f(b)$ is that of elements in $G_2$. The function $f$ is operation-preserving if it carries products into products. In this general setting, we say $f$ is operation-preserving if and only if the operation diagram below is valid.

EXAMPLE 2–37.　Let $(G_1, *)$ and $(G_2, \circ)$ be two arbitrary groups having identity elements $e_1$ and $e_2$ respectively. Define the function $f: G_1 \to G_2$ by $f(a) = e_2$ for each $a \in G_1$. Then

$$f(a * b) = e_2 = e_2 \circ e_2 = f(a) \circ f(b),$$

so that $f$ is operation-preserving.

EXAMPLE 2–38.　Consider the two groups $(R^{\#}, +)$ and $(R^{\#} - \{0\}, \cdot)$, where, as usual, $+$ and $\cdot$ denote ordinary addition and multiplication. For $a \in R^{\#}$, define the function $f$ by $f(a) = 2^a$. To show that the mapping is operation-preserving in this case, we must establish that $f(a + b) = f(a) \cdot f(b)$. This is readily verified, since

$$f(a + b) = 2^{a+b} = 2^a \cdot 2^b = f(a) \cdot f(b).$$

EXAMPLE 2–39.　Let $(Z, +)$ be the group of integers under addition and $(Z_n, +_n)$ be the group of integers modulo $n$. Define $f: Z \to Z_n$ by $f(a) = [a]$; that is, map each integer into the congruence class containing it. That $f$ is operation-preserving follows from the definition of modular addition:

$$f(a + b) = [a + b] = [a] +_n [b] = f(a) +_n f(b).$$

There are many important and interesting facts concerning operation-preserving functions. In the following theorems, we shall examine some of these results in detail.

**THEOREM 2–19.**　If $f$ is an operation-preserving function from the group $(G_1, *)$ into the group $(G_2, \circ)$, then

(1) $f$ maps the identity element $e_1$ of $(G_1, *)$ onto the identity element $e_2$ of $(G_2, \circ)$: $f(e_1) = e_2$;

(2) $f$ maps the inverse of an element $a \in G_1$ onto the inverse of $f(a)$: $f(a^{-1}) = f(a)^{-1}$ for each $a \in G_1$.

*Proof.* To prove the first assertion, it is enough to observe that under the hypothesis of the theorem,

$$f(a) \circ e_2 = f(a) = f(a * e_1) = f(a) \circ f(e_1)$$

whenever $a \in G_1$. By the cancellation law in $(G_2, \circ)$, we then have

$$f(e_1) = e_2.$$

In the second part of the theorem, it is first necessary to show that

$$f(a) \circ f(a^{-1}) = e_2 = f(a^{-1}) \circ f(a).$$

We can then conclude from the uniqueness of the inverse of $f(a)$ in $(G_2, \circ)$ that $f(a)^{-1} = f(a^{-1})$. To obtain this result, we make use of Part (1) to get

$$f(a) \circ f(a^{-1}) = f(a * a^{-1}) = f(e_1) = e_2.$$

Similarly, $f(a^{-1}) \circ f(a) = e_2$.

> **DEFINITION 2-21.** Let $f$ be an operation-preserving function from the group $(G_1, *)$ into the group $(G_2, \circ)$ and let $e_2$ be the identity element of $(G_2, \circ)$. The *kernel* of $f$, denoted by $\ker(f)$, is the set
>
> $$\ker(f) = \{a \in G_1 \mid f(a) = e_2\}.$$

Thus $\ker(f)$ consists of those elements in $G_1$ which are mapped by $f$ onto the identity element of the group $(G_2, \circ)$. Theorem 2-19 indicates that $\ker(f)$ is a nonempty subset of $G_1$, since $e_1 \in \ker(f)$. It may well happen, as Example 2-37 shows, that $\ker(f) = G_1$. Except for the function indicated there, the kernel is always a proper subset of $G_1$. Our next theorem establishes the algebraic nature of the pair $(\ker(f), *)$.

> **THEOREM 2-20.** If $f$ is an operation-preserving function from the group $(G_1, *)$ into the group $(G_2, \circ)$, then
>
> (1) the pair $(\ker(f), *)$ is a distinguished subgroup of $(G_1, *)$;
> (2) the pair $(f(G_1), \circ)$ is a subgroup of $(G_2, \circ)$.

*Proof.* Consider any two elements $a$ and $b$ of $\ker(f)$. By definition, we know that $f(a) = f(b) = e_2$, where $e_2$ is the identity element of $(G_2, \circ)$. Therefore

$$f(a * b^{-1}) = f(a) \circ f(b^{-1}) = f(a) \circ f(b)^{-1} = e_2 \circ e_2^{-1}$$
$$= e_2 \circ e_2 = e_2,$$

and consequently $a * b^{-1} \in \ker(f)$. By Theorem 2-10, this is a sufficient condition for $(\ker(f), *)$ to be a subgroup of $(G_1, *)$.

That $(\ker(f), *)$ is distinguished in $(G_1, *)$ is established by showing that whenever $a \in G_1$ and $b \in \ker(f)$, then $a * b * a^{-1} \in \ker(f)$; that is, we must prove that $f(a * b * a^{-1}) = e_2$. This verification is straightforward, since

$$f(a * b * a^{-1}) = f(a) \circ f(b) \circ f(a^{-1})$$
$$= f(a) \circ e_2 \circ f(a)^{-1} = e_2.$$

To obtain the second part of the theorem, recall the definition of $f(G_1)$:

$$f(G_1) = \{f(a) \mid a \in G_1\}.$$

Thus, if $a', b' \in f(G_1)$, then there exist elements $a$ and $b$ of $G_1$ such that $a' = f(a), b' = f(b)$. This means

$$a' \circ (b')^{-1} = f(a) \circ f(b)^{-1} = f(a) \circ f(b^{-1}) = f(a * b^{-1}),$$

where $a * b^{-1} \in G_1$. Our argument shows that $a' \circ (b')^{-1} \in f(G_1)$, from which we are able to conclude that $(f(G_1), \circ)$ is a subgroup of $(G_2, \circ)$.

In general, it is not possible to show that $(f(G_1), \circ)$ is distinguished in $(G_2, \circ)$. We would like to know that

$$f(a) \circ x \circ f(a)^{-1} \in f(G_1)$$

whenever $x \in G_2$. However, since $f$ is not necessarily an onto mapping, there is no way of replacing $x$ by some $f(b)$ to make use of the operation-preserving property of $f$.

EXAMPLE 2–40. As a simple illustration of the above theorem, consider the two groups $(Z, +)$ and $(R^{\#} - \{0\}, \cdot)$. The mapping $f: Z \to R^{\#} - \{0\}$, defined by

$$f(n) = 1 \text{ if } n \in Z_{\mathrm{e}}$$
$$= -1 \text{ if } n \in Z_0$$

is operation-preserving, as the reader may verify by checking the various cases that could arise.

Here, $\ker(f) = \{n \in Z \mid f(n) = 1\} = Z_{\mathrm{e}}$, while the direct image $f(Z) = \{1, -1\}$. It is not particularly difficult to show that $(Z_{\mathrm{e}}, +)$ is a distinguished subgroup of $(Z, +)$ and that $(\{1, -1\}, \cdot)$ is a subgroup of $(R^{\#} - \{0\}, \cdot)$.

Our definition of an operation-preserving function did not require that it be a one-to-one mapping and, indeed, we have presented several examples where it failed to be so. There is, however, a simple characterization of a one-to-one operation-preserving function in terms of the kernel.

**THEOREM 2–21.** Let $f$ be an operation-preserving function from the group $(G_1, *)$ into the group $(G_2, \circ)$. Then $f$ is one-to-one if and only if $\ker(f) = \{e_1\}$.

*Proof.* Suppose the function $f$ is one-to-one. We already know that $e_1 \in \ker(f)$. Our aim is to show that this is the only element in the kernel. If there existed another element $a \in \ker(f)$, $a \neq e_1$, then we would have $f(a) = e_2 = f(e_1)$. That is, $f(a) = f(e_1)$ but $a \neq e_1$. This would contradict the hypothesis that $f$ is one-to-one.

On the other hand, suppose that $\ker(f) = \{e_1\}$. Let $a, b \in G_1$ and $f(a) = f(b)$. To prove $f$ is one-to-one, we must show that $a = b$. But if $f(a) = f(b)$, then

$$f(a * b^{-1}) = f(a) \circ f(b^{-1}) = f(a) \circ f(b)^{-1}$$
$$= f(a) \circ f(a)^{-1} = e_2,$$

which implies $a * b^{-1} \in \ker(f)$. But $\ker(f) = \{e_1\}$. Therefore $a * b^{-1} = e_1$ or $a = b$.

**DEFINITION 2–22.** Two groups $(G_1, *)$ and $(G_2, \circ)$ are said to be *algebraically equivalent* (or *isomorphic*), denoted by writing $(G_1, *) \simeq (G_2, \circ)$, if there exists a one-to-one operation-preserving function $f$ of $(G_1, *)$ onto $(G_2, \circ)$; that is, if $f(G_1) = G_2$.

Any property of $(G_1, *)$ which can be expressed in terms of the operation $*$ is preserved under $f$ and is consequently also a property of $(G_2, \circ)$. Thus algebraically equivalent groups are indistinguishable from the abstract point of view, even though they may differ in the notation for their elements and operations.

Actually, the concept of algebraic equivalence is applicable to all types of mathematical systems, for it seems reasonable that we should wish to treat two systems as essentially equal when they have exactly the same properties. The essence of the notion is that we can always find a one-to-one mapping between the elements of the two systems which preserves the algebraic structure.

EXAMPLE 2–41. Consider the two groups $(Z_4, +_4)$ and $(G, \cdot)$, where $G = \{1, -1, i, -i\}$ and $i^2 = -1$. The operation tables for these two systems are:

| $+_4$ | 0 | 1 | 2 | 3 |
|-------|---|---|---|---|
| 0 | 0 | 1 | 2 | 3 |
| 1 | 1 | 2 | 3 | 0 |
| 2 | 2 | 3 | 0 | 1 |
| 3 | 3 | 0 | 1 | 2 |

| $\cdot$ | 1 | $-1$ | $i$ | $-i$ |
|---------|---|------|-----|------|
| 1 | 1 | $-1$ | $i$ | $-i$ |
| $-1$ | $-1$ | 1 | $-i$ | $i$ |
| $i$ | $i$ | $-i$ | $-1$ | 1 |
| $-i$ | $-i$ | $i$ | 1 | $-1$ |

We wish to prove that the groups $(Z_4, +_4)$ and $(G, \cdot)$ are abstractly equal. To do so, we must produce a one-to-one operation-preserving function $f$ from $Z_4$ onto $G$.

Since the preservation of identity elements is a general feature of operation-preserving functions, $f$ must be such that $f(0) = 1$. Let us suppose for the moment that we were to define $f(1) = -1$. The image of an inverse element must equal the inverse of the image. We would then have

$$f(3) = f(1^{-1}) = f(1)^{-1} = (-1)^{-1} = -1$$

or $f(3) = f(1)$. This, however, would prevent $f$ from being one-to-one.

A more appropriate choice, in the sense that it avoids the above difficulty, is to take $f(1) = i$. The condition on inverses then implies $f(3) = -i$. Since $f$ is further required to preserve modular addition,

$$f(2) = f(1 +_4 1) = f(1) \cdot f(1) = i \cdot i = -1.$$

We are thus led in a natural way to consider the function defined by:

$$f(0) = 1, \quad f(1) = i, \quad f(2) = -1, \quad f(3) = -i.$$

Clearly this function is a one-to-one mapping of the set $Z_4$ onto the set $G$. Furthermore, $f$ actually preserves the operations of the groups. Merely to verify one instance, we observe that

$$f(1 +_4 2) = f(3) = -i = i \cdot -1 = f(1) \cdot f(2).$$

Consequently, we have $(Z_4, +_4) \simeq (G, \cdot)$.

It is worth noting that $(Z_4, +_4)$ is also algebraically equivalent to $(G, \cdot)$ under the function $g$, where

$$g(0) = 1, \quad g(1) = -i, \quad g(2) = -1, \quad g(3) = i.$$

EXAMPLE 2–42. Let $G = \{x, y, z, w\}$ and the operation $*$ be defined by the table

| $*$ | $x$ | $y$ | $z$ | $w$ |
|---|---|---|---|---|
| $x$ | $x$ | $y$ | $z$ | $w$ |
| $y$ | $y$ | $x$ | $w$ | $z$ |
| $z$ | $z$ | $w$ | $x$ | $y$ |
| $w$ | $w$ | $z$ | $y$ | $x$ |

The reader may verify that $(G, *)$ is a group. The two groups $(Z_4, +_4)$ and $(G, *)$ are not abstractly equal, however, for every one-to-one function $f$ from the set $Z_4$ onto $G$ fails to be operation-preserving. From this we conclude that there are at least two distinct algebraic structures for groups with four elements.

To illustrate this point, we check several possibilities for the function $f$. Consider the mapping defined on the set $Z_4$ by

$$f(0) = x, \quad f(1) = y, \quad f(2) = z, \quad f(3) = w.$$

Then

$$f(1 +_4 3) = f(0) = x \neq z = y * w = f(1) * f(3),$$

which shows that $f$ is not operation-preserving. Another possibility for $f$ might be

$$f(0) = x, \quad f(1) = z, \quad f(2) = w, \quad f(3) = y.$$

Note that we must always map identity elements to identity elements. This choice of $f$ also fails to preserve the operations, since

$$f(1 +_4 1) = f(2) = w \neq x = z * z = f(1) * f(1).$$

We shall leave the test of the remaining possibilities as an exercise.

EXAMPLE 2–43. At one time or another, the following three groups have been considered: $(G_1, \circ)$, where

$$G_1 = \{x, -x, 1/x, -1/x\}$$

and $\circ$ denotes functional composition; $(G_2, *)$, where

$$G_2 = \{R_{360}, R_{180}, H, V\}$$

and $*$ consists of following one symmetry of the square by another; $(G_3, \cdot_{12})$, where

$$G_3 = \{1, 5, 7, 11\}.$$

The operation tables for these groups are defined in Table 2–5.

TABLE 2–5

| $\circ$ | $x$ | $-x$ | $1/x$ | $-1/x$ |
|---|---|---|---|---|
| $x$ | $x$ | $-x$ | $1/x$ | $-1/x$ |
| $-x$ | $-x$ | $x$ | $-1/x$ | $1/x$ |
| $1/x$ | $1/x$ | $-1/x$ | $x$ | $-x$ |
| $-1/x$ | $-1/x$ | $1/x$ | $-x$ | $x$ |

| $\cdot_{12}$ | 1 | 5 | 7 | 11 |
|---|---|---|---|---|
| 1 | 1 | 5 | 7 | 11 |
| 5 | 5 | 1 | 11 | 7 |
| 7 | 7 | 11 | 1 | 5 |
| 11 | 11 | 7 | 5 | 1 |

| $*$ | $R_{360}$ | $R_{180}$ | $H$ | $V$ |
|---|---|---|---|---|
| $R_{360}$ | $R_{360}$ | $R_{180}$ | $H$ | $V$ |
| $R_{180}$ | $R_{180}$ | $R_{360}$ | $V$ | $H$ |
| $H$ | $H$ | $V$ | $R_{360}$ | $R_{180}$ |
| $V$ | $V$ | $H$ | $R_{180}$ | $R_{360}$ |

The groups $(G_1, \circ)$, $(G_2, *)$, and $(G_3, \cdot_{12})$ are all algebraically equivalent; they have the same algebraic structure as the group $(G, \cdot)$, where $G = \{a, b, c, d\}$ and $\cdot$ is defined by

| $\cdot$ | $a$ | $b$ | $c$ | $d$ |
|---|---|---|---|---|
| $a$ | $a$ | $b$ | $c$ | $d$ |
| $b$ | $b$ | $a$ | $d$ | $c$ |
| $c$ | $c$ | $d$ | $a$ | $b$ |
| $d$ | $d$ | $c$ | $b$ | $a$ |

The following one-to-one correspondences preserve the group operations:

$$a \leftrightarrow x \leftrightarrow R_{360} \leftrightarrow 1,$$
$$b \leftrightarrow -x \leftrightarrow R_{180} \leftrightarrow 5,$$
$$c \leftrightarrow 1/x \leftrightarrow H \leftrightarrow 7,$$
$$d \leftrightarrow -1/x \leftrightarrow V \leftrightarrow 11.$$

EXAMPLE 2–44. The two groups $(Z, +)$ and $(Q - \{0\}, \cdot)$ are not algebraically equivalent. To see this, suppose that there exists a one-to-one onto function $f: Z \to Q - \{0\}$ with the property

$$f(a + b) = f(a) \cdot f(b)$$

for all $a, b \in Z$. If $x$ denotes the element of $Z$ such that $f(x) = -1$, then

$$f(2x) = f(x + x) = f(x) \cdot f(x) = (-1) \cdot (-1) = 1.$$

According to Theorem 2–21, the identity element of $(Z, +)$ is the unique element of $Z$ corresponding to the identity of $(Q - \{0\}, \cdot)$, so that $2x = 0$ or $x = 0$. Consequently, both $f(0) = 1$ and $f(0) = -1$, contradicting the fact that the function $f$ is one-to-one. This argument shows that $(Z, +)$ cannot be algebraically equivalent to $(Q - \{0\}, \cdot)$, for no function satisfying Definition 2–22 can exist.

Every group $(G, *)$ is algebraically equivalent to itself under the identity mapping $f(x) = x$, $x \in G$. A natural question is whether $(G, *)$ is equivalent to any group other than itself. Our next theorem, a classical result due to Cayley, answers this question in the affirmative.

For each element $a$ of $G$, let $f_a$ be the mapping of the set $G$ into itself:

$$f_a(x) = a * x, \qquad x \in G.$$

We denote the collection of all such left-multiplication functions by $F_G$:

$$F_G = \{f_a \mid a \in G\}.$$

The reader may recall that in Example 2–26, it was shown that the pair $(F_G, \circ)$ forms a group, where $\circ$ indicates the operation of functional composition. We shall prove that $(G, *)$ is algebraically equivalent to $(F_G, \circ)$.

**THEOREM 2–22 (Cayley).** If $(G, *)$ is an arbitrary group, then $(G, *) \simeq (F_G, \circ)$.

*Proof.* Define the mapping $f\colon G \to F_G$ by the rule $f(a) = f_a$ for each $a \in G$. That the function $f$ is onto $F_G$ is obvious. If $f_a = f_b$, then $a * x = b * x$ for all elements $x$ of $G$. In particular,

$$a = a * e = b * e = b,$$

which shows that $f$ is one-to-one. We complete the proof by establishing that $f$ is operation-preserving:

$$f(a * b) = f_{a*b} = f_a \circ f_b = f(a) \circ f(b).$$

As an illustration of this theorem, consider the group $(R^{\#}, +)$. Corresponding to an element $a \in R^{\#}$ is the left-multiplication function $f_a$, defined by $f_a(x) = a + x$, $x \in R^{\#}$. That is, the function $f_a$ merely has the effect of translating or shifting elements by an amount $a$. Cayley's Theorem asserts that the group $(R^{\#}, +)$ and the group $(F_G, \circ)$ of translations of the real line are indistinguishable as far as their algebraic properties are concerned.

We shall conclude our study of groups with two theorems which relate a number of concepts previously investigated. In Theorem 2–20, it was seen that every operation-preserving function determines a distinguished subgroup through its kernel. The first of the following two theorems shows that every distinguished subgroup determines an operation-preserving function, the so-called *natural mapping*.

**THEOREM 2–23.** Let $(H, *)$ be a distinguished subgroup of the group $(G, *)$. Then the mapping $f\colon G \to G/H$, defined by $f(a) = a * H$, is an operation-preserving function from $(G, *)$ onto the quotient group $(G/H, \otimes)$ having $H$ as its kernel.

*Proof.* The fact that the function $f$ is operation-preserving follows directly from the definition of the operation in the quotient group:

$$f(a * b) = (a * b) * H = (a * H) \otimes (b * H) = f(a) \otimes f(b).$$

Inasmuch as the coset $H$ acts as the identity for $(G/H, \otimes)$, we have

$$\ker(f) = \{a \in G \mid f(a) = H\} = \{a \in G \mid a * H = H\} = H.$$

To obtain this last equality, Theorem 2–13 has been employed.

It should be observed that the natural mapping is not necessarily one-to-one. For if the elements $a, b \in G$ are such that the product $a * b^{-1}$ is in $H$, then according to Theorem 2–14, $a * H = b * H$ and consequently $f(a) = f(b)$.

Our final theorem indicates that any operation-preserving function from a group $(G_1, *)$ onto a second group $(G_2, \circ)$ induces in a natural way an operation-preserving function under which $(G_2, \circ)$ is algebraically equivalent to some quotient group of $G_1$. We state the precise result as follows:

> **THEOREM 2–24.** Let $f$ be an operation-preserving function from the group $(G_1, *)$ onto the group $(G_2, \circ)$. Then the quotient group $(G_1/\ker(f), \otimes) \simeq (G_2, \circ)$ under the mapping $\bar{f}: G_1/\ker(f) \to G_2$, defined by
>
> $$\bar{f}(a * \ker(f)) = f(a).$$

We shall leave the details of the proof to the reader and merely show that the function $\bar{f}$ depends only on the cosets of $\ker(f)$ and in no way on the representatives chosen from these sets. To see this, suppose that $a * \ker(f) = b * \ker(f)$. Since $a$ and $b$ are elements of the same coset of $\ker(f)$, $a * b^{-1} \in \ker(f)$. This means that

$$f(a) = f(a * b^{-1} * b) = f(a * b^{-1}) \circ f(b) = e_2 \circ f(b) = f(b),$$

and consequently by the definition of $\bar{f}$ that

$$\bar{f}(a * \ker(f)) = \bar{f}(b * \ker(f)).$$

Theorem 2–24 is admittedly rather technical in nature and therefore perhaps a brief explanation of its significance is in order. Suppose that $(G_1, *)$ is an unfamiliar group whose algebraic properties we wish to determine. Clearly, if $(G_1, *)$ could be shown to be algebraically equivalent to some well-known group $(G_2, \circ)$, then our problem is solved, for $(G_1, *)$, being a replica of $(G_2, \circ)$, would possess the same algebraic structure.

Another approach, which usually gives a less complete picture of $(G_1, *)$ is to examine its images under operation-preserving functions. The difficulty here, of course, is that when these functions fail to be one-to-one, not all the algebraic properties of the images are reflected in the original group. For instance, it is quite possible for the commutative law to hold in an image group without $(G_1, *)$ itself being commutative. Theorem 2–24 asserts that the images of $(G_1, *)$ under operation-preserving functions can be duplicated with algebraic equivalence by quotient groups of $(G_1, *)$. In a sense, it is not necessary to go beyond $(G_1, *)$ to obtain all its images under operation-preserving functions.

This finishes our study of groups. We have not attempted to range over the whole field of group theory nor to examine in depth any particular aspect of it. Instead we have introduced the reader to a few of the high points. Needless to say, current research in this branch of mathematics is both vigorous and extensive. A variety of classical problems still remain unsolved, while in some directions the research has only recently begun.

## PROBLEMS

1. In the following cases, check that the indicated function is operation-preserving from the first group onto the second group:

   (a) $f(a) = a/2$, $(Z, +)$, $(Z, +)$
   (b) $f(a) = -a$, $(Z, +)$, $(Z, +)$
   (c) $f(a) = a^2$, $(R^{\#} - \{0\}, \cdot)$, $(R^{\#}_{+}, \cdot)$
   (d) $f(a) = a/q$ ($q$ a fixed nonzero integer), $(Z, +)$, $(Q, +)$

2. Let the set $G = Z \times Z$ and the binary operation $*$ on $G$ be given by the rule $(a, b) * (c, d) = (a + c, b + d)$. It is easily verified that the pair $(G, *)$ is a commutative group.

   (a) Show that the mapping $f: G \to Z$ defined by

   $$f[(a, b)] = a$$

   is an operation-preserving function from $(G, *)$ onto the group $(Z, +)$.
   (b) Determine the kernel of this mapping.
   (c) If $H = \{(a, a) \mid a \in Z\}$, prove that $(H, *)$ is a subgroup of $(G, *)$ and is algebraically equivalent to $(Z, +)$ under the function $f$.

3. Suppose $f$ is an operation-preserving function from the group $(G_1, *_1)$ onto the group $(G_2, *_2)$ and $g$ is an operation-preserving function from $(G_2, *_2)$ onto the group $(G_3, *_3)$. Prove that the composite function $g \circ f$ is operation-preserving from $(G_1, *_1)$ onto $(G_3, *_3)$.

4. Consider the two groups $(Z, +)$ and $(\{1, -1, i, -i\}, \cdot)$, where $i^2 = -1$. Show that the mapping defined by $f(n) = i^n$ for $n \in Z$ is an operation-preserving function from $(Z, +)$ onto $(\{1, -1, i, -i\}, \cdot)$, and determine its kernel.

5. Let $(G, *)$ be a group and $a \in G$. Prove that the group $(G, *)$ is algebraically equivalent to itself; that is, $(G, *) \simeq (G, *)$ under the mapping $f$ defined by

   $$f(x) = a * x * a^{-1}, \quad x \in G.$$

6. Let $(G, *)$ be a group and $f$ be the mapping of the set $G$ onto itself defined by $f(a) = a^{-1}$, $a \in G$. Prove that $f$ is operation-preserving if and only if $(G, *)$ is commutative.

7. Prove that if the group $(G_1, *)$ is commutative and $(G_1, *) \simeq (G_2, \circ)$, then the group $(G_2, \circ)$ is also commutative.

8. Show that the two groups $(R^\#, +)$ and $(R^\# - \{0\}, \cdot)$ are not algebraically equivalent.

9. Prove that all finite groups of order two are algebraically equivalent.

10. Given

$$G = \left\{ 1, \frac{-1 + i\sqrt{3}}{2}, \frac{-1 - i\sqrt{3}}{2} \right\},$$

the pair $(G, \cdot)$ is a group, where $i^2 = -1$ as usual. Determine whether $(G, \cdot) \simeq (Z_3, +_3)$.

11. Let $f$ be an operation-preserving function from the group $(G, *)$ into itself and let $H$ denote the set of elements of $G$ which are left fixed by $f$:

$$H = \{a \in G \mid f(a) = a\}.$$

Prove that $(H, *)$ is a subgroup of $(G, *)$.

12. Suppose $f$ is an operation-preserving function from the group $(G_1, *)$ into the group $(G_2, \circ)$.

    (a) Show that if $(H, *)$ is a subgroup of $(G_1, *)$, then $\big(f(H), \circ\big)$ is a subgroup of $(G_2, \circ)$.

    (b) Let $(K, \circ)$ be a distinguished subgroup of the group $(G_2, \circ)$. Prove that the pair $\big(f^{-1}(K), *\big)$ is a distinguished subgroup of $(G_1, *)$, where

$$f^{-1}(K) = \{a \in G_1 \mid f(a) \in K\}.$$

13. Let $f$ and $g$ be two operation-preserving functions from the group $(G_1, *)$ into the group $(G_2, \circ)$. Define the function $h: G_1 \to G_2$ by

$$h(a) = f(a) \circ g(a).$$

Show that if the group $(G_2, \circ)$ is commutative, then $h$ is also operation preserving.

14. Let $f$ be an operation-preserving function from the group $(G_1, *)$ onto the group $(G_2, \circ)$. Given that $f$ is a one-to-one function, prove that its inverse $f^{-1}$ is an operation-preserving function from $(G_2, \circ)$ onto $(G_1, *)$. This result together with Problem 3 above may be used to show that the set of all operation-preserving functions and the operation of functional composition form a group.

*Chapter 3*

# MATHEMATICAL SYSTEMS
# WITH TWO OPERATIONS

### 3-1. RINGS: DEFINITIONS AND
### ELEMENTARY PROPERTIES

In this chapter, we shall investigate algebraic systems having two suitably restricted binary operations. Obvious examples are the familiar number systems of elementary mathematics (the integers, the rational numbers, etc.) and the algebra of sets.

Using these systems as models, we shall presently define an algebraic structure known as a ring. Inasmuch as a ring is basically a combination of a commutative group and a semigroup, our previous experience with groups will prove to be of considerable help. As the reader will see, many of the important notions in group theory have natural extensions to systems with two operations.

It is necessary to adopt some axioms which interrelate the two binary operations of our systems. These axioms are the so-called "distributive laws."

**DEFINITION 3-1.** Let $(S, *, \circ)$ be a mathematical system with binary operations $*$ and $\circ$. The operation $\circ$ is said to be *distributive* over the operation $*$ if

$$a \circ (b * c) = (a \circ b) * (a \circ c) \qquad \text{(left distributive law)}$$

and

$$(b * c) \circ a = (b \circ a) * (c \circ a) \qquad \text{(right distributive law)}$$

for every triple of elements $a, b, c \in S$.

If the operation ∘ happens to be commutative, then whenever ∘ is left distributive over the operation *, it is also right distributive (and conversely), since

$$(b * c) \circ a = a \circ (b * c) = (a \circ b) * (a \circ c) = (b \circ a) * (c \circ a).$$

Clearly, ordinary multiplication is distributive over ordinary addition, and we use this fact in the next example.

EXAMPLE 3-1. Consider two binary operations * and ∘ defined on the set $Z$ of integers by $a * b = a + 2b$, $a \circ b = 2ab$. A simple calculation shows the operation ∘ to be left distributive over *, for

$$a \circ (b * c) = a \circ (b + 2c) = 2a(b + 2c) = 2ab + 4ac,$$

while

$$(a \circ b) * (a \circ c) = (2ab) * (2ac) = 2ab + 2(2ac)$$
$$= 2ab + 4ac.$$

Because ∘ is a commutative operation, we conclude that it is also right distributive over *.

**DEFINITION 3-2.** A *ring* is a mathematical system $(R, *, \circ)$ consisting of a nonempty set $R$ and two binary operations * and ∘ defined on $R$ such that

(1) $(R, *)$ is a commutative group;
(2) $(R, \circ)$ is a semigroup;
(3) the semigroup operation ∘ is distributive over the group operation *.

It is convenient and customary to use $+$ for the group operation and $\cdot$ for the semigroup operation, rather than the symbols * and ∘. This convention is longstanding and is particularly helpful in emphasizing the analogy between results obtained for rings and those of the familiar number systems. The above definition then takes the form:

**DEFINITION 3-3.** A ring $(R, +, \cdot)$ is a nonempty set $R$ with two binary operations $+$ and $\cdot$ on $R$ such that

(1) $(R, +)$ is a commutative group;
(2) $(R, \cdot)$ is a semigroup;
(3) the two operations are related by the distributive laws

$a \cdot (b + c) = (a \cdot b) + (a \cdot c)$
$(b + c) \cdot a = (b \cdot a) + (c \cdot a)$

for all $a, b, c \in R$.

The reader should clearly understand that $+$ and $\cdot$ represent abstract unspecified operations and not ordinary addition and multiplication. For convenience, however, we shall refer to the operation $+$ as "addition" and the operation $\cdot$ as "multiplication." In the light of this terminology, it is natural then to speak of the commutative group $(R, +)$ as being the *additive group* of the ring and $(R, \cdot)$ the *multiplicative semigroup* of the ring.

The unique identity element for addition is called the *zero element* of the ring and is denoted by the usual symbol for zero, 0. The unique additive inverse of an element $a \in R$ shall be written as $-a$.

In order to minimize the use of parentheses in expressions involving both operations, we make the stipulation that multiplication is to be performed before addition. Thus the expression $a \cdot b + c$ stands for $(a \cdot b) + c$ and not for $a \cdot (b + c)$.

With this notation in mind, we can now rephrase our current definition of ring in a more detailed form: A ring $(R, +, \cdot)$ consists of a nonempty set $R$ and two operations, called addition and multiplication and denoted by $+$ and $\cdot$, respectively, satisfying the requirements:

(1) $R$ is closed under addition,

(2) $a + b = b + a$,

(3) $(a + b) + c = a + (b + c)$,

(4) there exists an element 0 in $R$ such that $a + 0 = a$ for every $a \in R$,

(5) for each $a \in R$, there exists an element $-a \in R$ such that

$$a + (-a) = 0,$$

(6) $R$ is closed under multiplication,

(7) $(a \cdot b) \cdot c = a \cdot (b \cdot c)$,

(8) $a \cdot (b + c) = a \cdot b + a \cdot c$ and $(b + c) \cdot a = b \cdot a + c \cdot a$,

where it is understood that $a$, $b$, $c$ represent arbitrary elements of $R$.

By placing further restrictions on the operation of multiplication, several special types of rings are obtained.

**DEFINITION 3–4.** (1) A *commutative ring* is a ring in which $(R, \cdot)$ is a commutative semigroup; that is, the operation of multiplication is commutative. (2) A *ring with identity* is a ring in which $(R, \cdot)$ is a semigroup with identity; that is, there exists an identity element for the operation of multiplication, customarily denoted by the symbol 1.

In a ring $(R, +, \cdot)$ with identity, if an element $a \in R$ has a multiplicative inverse, it shall be denoted as before by $a^{-1}$. Multiplicative inverses are unique (Problem 6) when they exist.

Before proceeding to the proofs of some of the basic results of ring theory, we shall consider several examples.

EXAMPLE 3–2. Each of the following systems, where $+$ and $\cdot$ indicate ordinary addition and multiplication, is a commutative ring:

$$(R^{\#}, +, \cdot), \qquad (Q, +, \cdot),$$
$$(Z, +, \cdot), \qquad (Z_{\mathrm{e}}, +, \cdot).$$

The first three of these rings have an identity element, the integer 1, for multiplication.

EXAMPLE 3–3. If $R_U$ denotes the family of all subsets of some nonempty universe $U$, then the triples $(R_U, \cup, \cap)$ and $(R_U, \cap, \cup)$ do not form rings, for neither $(R_U, \cup)$ nor $(R_U, \cap)$ constitutes a group. The reader may recall, however, that in Example 2–21 the pair $(R_U, *)$ was shown to be a commutative group, where $*$ was the symmetric difference operation

$$A * B = (A - B) \cup (B - A).$$

Since $(R_U, \cap)$ is clearly a commutative semigroup, in order to establish that $(R_U, *, \cap)$ is a ring we need only verify that $\cap$ is left distributive over $*$. This is not particularly difficult, for if $A, B,$ and $C$ are subsets of $U$, then

$$
\begin{aligned}
A \cap (B * C) &= A \cap [(B - C) \cup (C - B)] \\
&= [A \cap (B - C)] \cup [A \cap (C - B)] \\
&= [(A \cap B) - (A \cap C)] \cup [(A \cap C) - (A \cap B)] \\
&= (A \cap B) * (A \cap C).
\end{aligned}
$$

In the above argument, we utilized the set identity (see Problem 6, p. 6)

$$A \cap (B - C) = (A \cap B) - (A \cap C).$$

EXAMPLE 3–4. Let $R$ denote the set of all functions from the real numbers into the reals. The sum $f + g$ and product $f \cdot g$ of two functions $f, g \in R$ are defined by specifying the value of these combinations at each real number:

$$(f + g)(a) = f(a) + g(a),$$
$$(f \cdot g)(a) = f(a) \cdot g(a).$$

That $(R, +, \cdot)$ is a commutative ring with identity follows from the fact that the real numbers with ordinary addition and multiplication constitute such a system. In particular, the multiplicative identity is the constant function whose range value consists of the single real number 1.

It is interesting to note that the triple $(R, +, \circ)$, where $\circ$ indicates the operation of functional composition, fails to be a ring. The left distributive law

$$f \circ (g + h) = (f \circ g) + (f \circ h)$$

does not hold in this case.

EXAMPLE 3–5. Still another example of a ring is provided by the set

$$R = \{a + b\sqrt{3} \mid a, b \in Z\}$$

and the operations of ordinary addition and multiplication. The set $R$ is obviously closed under these operations, for

$$(a + b\sqrt{3}) + (c + d\sqrt{3}) = (a + c) + (b + d)\sqrt{3} \in R,$$
$$(a + b\sqrt{3}) \cdot (c + d\sqrt{3}) = (ac + 3bd) + (ad + bc)\sqrt{3} \in R,$$

whenever $a, b, c, d \in Z$. We omit the details of showing that $(R, +, \cdot)$ is a commutative ring with identity element $1 = 1 + 0\sqrt{3} \in R$.

EXAMPLE 3–6. In Section 2–3, we considered the group $(Z_n, +_n)$ of integers modulo $n$. This group was obtained on defining in the set $Z_n$ the notion of addition of congruence classes:

$$[a] +_n [b] = [a + b].$$

A binary operation $\cdot_n$ of multiplication of classes may equally well be introduced in $Z_n$ by specifying that for each pair of elements $[a], [b] \in Z_n$

$$[a] \cdot_n [b] = [a \cdot b].$$

This latter definition presents a problem similar to that of addition in that we must show that the resulting product $[a \cdot b]$ is independent of the particular representatives chosen from the congruence classes $[a]$ and $[b]$. In other words, it must be established that whenever $[a'] = [a]$ and $[b'] = [b]$,

$$[a' \cdot b'] = [a \cdot b].$$

We first observe that $a' \in [a'] = [a]$ and $b' \in [b'] = [b]$ imply that

$$a' \equiv a \pmod{n}, \qquad b' \equiv b \pmod{n}.$$

From Theorem 2–7 we are then able to conclude that

$$a' \cdot b' \equiv a \cdot b \pmod{n},$$

and consequently $a' \cdot b' \in [a \cdot b]$. This means, in view of Theorem 2–8, that $[a' \cdot b'] = [a \cdot b]$ as desired.

For each positive integer $n$, the system $(Z_n, +_n, \cdot_n)$ is a commutative ring with identity, known as the *ring of integers modulo n*. The verification that the ring axioms are satisfied is very straightforward, depending only on the definitions of the operations $+_n$ and $\cdot_n$ and the fact that $(Z, +, \cdot)$ itself is a ring.

For instance, to show the left distributivity of $\cdot_n$ over $+_n$, we choose $[a]$, $[b]$, $[c] \in Z_n$ and obtain

$$
\begin{aligned}
[a] \cdot_n ([b] +_n [c]) &= [a] \cdot_n [b + c] \\
&= [a \cdot (b + c)] \\
&= [a \cdot b + a \cdot c] \\
&= [a \cdot b] +_n [a \cdot c] \\
&= [a] \cdot_n [b] +_n [a] \cdot_n [c].
\end{aligned}
$$

Clearly [1] is the multiplicative identity element. We shall leave the verification of the remaining ring axioms and commutativity to the reader.

As mentioned earlier, it is convenient to remove the brackets in the designation of the congruence classes of $Z_n$, and this shall be our practice subsequently.

Since a ring $(R, +, \cdot)$ is a group under the operation of addition, all the results of the previous chapter on groups apply to the system $(R, +)$. For instance, we know that the zero element and additive inverses are unique, that the cancellation law holds for addition, and so on. In the theorems to follow, we shall establish some of the fundamental properties which depend on both ring operations. As usual, we know nothing about the specific nature of the system $(R, +, \cdot)$ except that it satisfies the postulates given in Definition 3–3.

**THEOREM 3–1.** In any ring $(R, +, \cdot)$, if $a \in R$, then

$$a \cdot 0 = 0 \cdot a = 0.$$

*Proof.* First note that an application of the left distributive law (and the fact that zero is the identity element for addition) yields

$$a \cdot 0 + a \cdot 0 = a \cdot (0 + 0) = a \cdot 0 = a \cdot 0 + 0.$$

By the cancellation law for addition,

$$a \cdot 0 = 0.$$

In similar fashion, one can show that $0 \cdot a = 0$.

Thus the product of two elements in a ring is zero whenever either factor is zero. The converse is not true. As the following examples will show, it may perfectly well happen that the product of two nonzero ring elements will be zero.

EXAMPLE 3-7.  Consider the set $R = R^{\#} \times R^{\#}$ of ordered pairs of real numbers. We define addition and multiplication on $R$ by the formulas

$$(a, b) + (c, d) = (a + c, b + d), \qquad (a, b) \cdot (c, d) = (ac, bd).$$

Then straightforward calculations will show that $(R, +, \cdot)$ is a commutative ring with identity element $(1, 1)$. Here the zero element is the pair $(0, 0)$. Observe that while

$$(1, 0) \cdot (0, 1) = (0, 0),$$

neither $(1, 0)$ nor $(0, 1)$ is the zero of the ring.

EXAMPLE 3-8.  Another example in which this situation occurs is the ring $(Z_4, +_4, \cdot_4)$ of integers modulo 4. The addition and multiplication tables are shown below:

| $+_4$ | 0 | 1 | 2 | 3 |
|-------|---|---|---|---|
| 0 | 0 | 1 | 2 | 3 |
| 1 | 1 | 2 | 3 | 0 |
| 2 | 2 | 3 | 0 | 1 |
| 3 | 3 | 0 | 1 | 2 |

| $\cdot_4$ | 0 | 1 | 2 | 3 |
|-----------|---|---|---|---|
| 0 | 0 | 0 | 0 | 0 |
| 1 | 0 | 1 | 2 | 3 |
| 2 | 0 | 2 | 0 | 2 |
| 3 | 0 | 3 | 2 | 1 |

Here we have $2 \cdot_4 2 = 0$, the product of nonzero elements being zero. Note also that $2 \cdot_4 1 = 2 \cdot_4 3$, yet it is clearly not true that $1 = 3$. The multiplicative semigroup $(Z_4, \cdot_4)$ fortunately does not satisfy the cancellation law.

> **DEFINITION 3-5.**  A ring $(R, +, \cdot)$ is said to have *divisors of zero* if there exist nonzero elements $a, b \in R$ such that the product $a \cdot b = 0$.

We exhibited two rings in the above examples which possess divisors of zero. The second example, in particular, suggests a relationship between the existence of divisors of zero and the failure of the cancellation law for multiplication. That this is indeed the case we shall see shortly.

First, several preliminary results concerning additive inverses are required. We shall adopt the usual convention of writing $a + (-b)$ as $a - b$ and refer to this expression as the *difference between a and b*.

**THEOREM 3–2.** Let $(R, +, \cdot)$ be a ring and $a, b \in R$. Then

$$-(a \cdot b) = a \cdot (-b) = (-a) \cdot b.$$

*Proof.* From the definition of additive inverse, we know that $b + (-b) = 0$. Using the left distributive law,

$$a \cdot b + a \cdot (-b) = a(b + (-b)) = a \cdot 0 = 0.$$

Inasmuch as the inverse of an element under addition is unique, this last equation implies that

$$-(a \cdot b) = a \cdot (-b).$$

A similar argument shows that $-(a \cdot b) = (-a) \cdot b$.

**COROLLARY.** For any elements $a, b \in R$,

$$(-a) \cdot (-b) = a \cdot b.$$

*Proof.* It follows from the above theorem that

$$(-a) \cdot (-b) = -((-a) \cdot b) = -(-(a \cdot b)) = a \cdot b.$$

The last equality stems from the fact that $(x^{-1})^{-1} = x$ in any group.

**COROLLARY.** If $a, b, c \in R$, then

$$a \cdot (b - c) = a \cdot b - a \cdot c, \qquad (b - c) \cdot a = b \cdot a - c \cdot a.$$

That is, multiplication is distributive over differences.

*Proof.* Since multiplication is left distributive over addition,

$$\begin{aligned}
a \cdot (b - c) &= a \cdot (b + (-c)) = a \cdot b + a \cdot (-c) \\
&= a \cdot b + (-(a \cdot c)) \\
&= a \cdot b - a \cdot c.
\end{aligned}$$

In a like manner, a right distributive law for differences is obtained.

Having thus laid the groundwork, we are now able to establish the following result.

**THEOREM 3–3.** The cancellation law for multiplication holds in any ring $(R, +, \cdot)$ having no divisors of zero. That is, if $a, b, c \in R$ with $a \neq 0$, then either $a \cdot b = a \cdot c$ or $b \cdot a = c \cdot a$ implies $b = c$.

*Proof.* Suppose, for instance, that $a \cdot b = a \cdot c$. Then

$$a \cdot (b - c) = a \cdot b - a \cdot c = 0.$$

Since $a \neq 0$ and $(R, +, \cdot)$ contains no divisors of zero, this last equation implies $b - c = 0$, or rather $b = c$. The other part of the theorem is handled in a like manner.

> **DEFINITION 3–6.** An *integral domain* is a commutative ring with identity which does not have divisors of zero.

We have just shown that the cancellation law for multiplication is valid in any integral domain.

A natural question which may have occurred to the reader is whether, in a ring with identity, the identity and zero elements of the ring are ever equal. We shall conclude this section by proving that this can only happen for the one-element ring $(\{0\}, +, \cdot)$.

> **THEOREM 3–4.** Let $(R, +, \cdot)$ be a ring with identity such that $R \neq \{0\}$. Then the elements 0 and 1 are distinct.

*Proof.* Since $R \neq \{0\}$, there exists some nonzero element $a \in R$. Now, if $1 = 0$, it would follow that

$$a = a \cdot 1 = a \cdot 0 = 0,$$

which is an obvious contradiction.

Unless stated to the contrary, we shall tacitly assume that *our rings contain more than one element.*

## PROBLEMS

1. Define two binary operations $*$ and $\circ$ on the set $Z$ by

   $$a * b = a + b + 2, \qquad a \circ b = ab + 2a + 2b + 2.$$

   Show that $\circ$ is distributive over $*$.

2. Let $(R, +)$ be any commutative group. Determine whether $(R, +, \cdot)$ is a ring if multiplication is defined by
   (a) $a \cdot b = a$,
   (b) $a \cdot b = 0$, where 0 is the identity element of the group $(R, +)$.

3. Given $a$, $b$, $c$, $d$ are elements of a ring $(R, +, \cdot)$, prove that:
   (a) $(a + b) \cdot (c + d) = a \cdot c + b \cdot c + a \cdot d + b \cdot d$

(b) $-(a \cdot b \cdot c) = (-a) \cdot (-b) \cdot (-c)$

(c) If $a \cdot b = b \cdot a = 0$, then $(a + b)^n = a^n + b^n$ for $n \in Z_+$  (As usual, $a^n = a \cdot a \cdots a$, $n$ times.)

4. Define two binary operations $*$ and $\circ$ on the set $Z$ of integers as follows:

$$a * b = a + b - 1, \qquad a \circ b = a + b - ab.$$

Prove that the system $(Z, *, \circ)$ is a commutative ring with identity.

5. Let $R$ be the set of all ordered pairs of nonzero real numbers. In the following cases, determine whether $(R, +, \cdot)$ is a commutative ring with identity. For those systems failing to be so, indicate which axioms are not satisfied.

(a) $(a, b) + (c, d) = (ac, bc + d)$, $(a, b) \cdot (c, d) = (ac, bd)$

(b) $(a, b) + (c, d) = (a + c, b + d)$, $(a, b) \cdot (c, d) = (ac + bc, ad + bd)$

(c) $(a, b) + (c, d) = (ad + bc, bd)$, $(a, b) \cdot (c, d) = (ac, bd)$

6. In a ring $(R, +, \cdot)$ with identity, prove that:

(a) The multiplicative identity element is unique.

(b) If $a \in R$ has a multiplicative inverse, then $a^{-1}$ is unique.

(c) If $G$ denotes the set of elements of $R$ with multiplicative inverses, then $(G, \cdot)$ is a group.

7. Let $(R, +, \cdot)$ be a ring which has the property that $a^2 = a$ for every $a \in R$. Prove that $(R, +, \cdot)$ is a commutative ring. [*Hint:* First show $a + a = 0$ for any $a \in R$.]

8. For an element $a$ in a ring $(R, +, \cdot)$ and $n \in Z_+$, define

$$na = a + a + \cdots + a \qquad (n \text{ times}),$$
$$(-n)a = -(na).$$

Show that $n(a \cdot b) = (na) \cdot b = a \cdot (nb)$ for all $n \in Z$.

9. Prove that a ring $(R, +, \cdot)$ is commutative if and only if

$$(a + b)^2 = a^2 + 2a \cdot b + b^2$$

for every pair of elements $a, b \in R$.

10. Discover divisors of zero to show that $(Z_6, +_6, \cdot_6)$ is not an integral domain. More generally, show that $(Z_n, +_n, \cdot_n)$ contains divisors of zero if $n$ is not prime.

11. An element $a$ of a ring $(R, +, \cdot)$ is said to be *nilpotent* if $a^n = 0$ for some $n \in Z_+$. Prove that in an integral domain the zero element is the only nilpotent element.

12. Let $(R_1, *_1, \circ_1)$ and $(R_2, *_2, \circ_2)$ be two rings. Define two binary operations $+$ and $\cdot$ on the Cartesian product $R_1 \times R_2$ as follows:

$$(a, b) + (c, d) = (a *_1 c, b *_2 d), \qquad (a, b) \cdot (c, d) = (a \circ_1 c, b \circ_2 d).$$

Prove that the system $(R_1 \times R_2, +, \cdot)$ is a ring. If the original rings are commutative with identity, show that this is also true of $(R_1 \times R_2, +, \cdot)$.

## 3–2.  SUBRINGS  AND  IDEALS

In Section 2–4, we discussed the concept of a subgroup of a group. It is natural that there should be a corresponding notion of subsystems for rings.

> **DEFINITION 3–7.** Let $(R, +, \cdot)$ be a ring and $S \subseteq R$ be a nonempty subset of $R$. If, using the same operations, the triple $(S, +, \cdot)$ is itself a ring, then $(S, +, \cdot)$ is said to be a *subring* of $(R, +, \cdot)$.

An examination of the definition of ring as given in 3–2 shows that $(S, +, \cdot)$ is a subring of $(R, +, \cdot)$ if $(S, +)$ is a subgroup of $(R, +)$, $(S, \cdot)$ is a subsemigroup of $(R, \cdot)$, and the two distributive laws hold for elements of $S$. But both the distributive and associative laws hold automatically in $S$ as a consequence of their validity in $R$. Since these laws are inherited from $R$, there is no particular necessity of requiring them in the definition of a subring.

In view of this observation, a subring could alternatively be defined as follows:

The triple $(S, +, \cdot)$ is a subring of the ring $(R, +, \cdot)$ whenever

(1)  $S$ is a nonempty subset of $R$,
(2)  $(S, +)$ is a subgroup of $(R, +)$,
(3)  $S$ is closed under multiplication.

Even this definition may be improved upon, for the reader may recall that if $\emptyset \neq H \subseteq G$, then the pair $(H, *)$ is a subgroup of the group $(G, *)$ provided that $a, b \in H$ implies $a * b^{-1} \in H$. Adjusting the notation to our present situation, we obtain a minimal set of conditions for determining subrings.

> **DEFINITION 3–8.** Let $(R, +, \cdot)$ be a ring and $\emptyset \neq S \subseteq R$. Then the triple $(S, +, \cdot)$ is a subring of $(R, +, \cdot)$ if and only if
>
> (1)  $a - b \in S$ whenever $a, b \in S$   (closed under differences),
> (2)  $a \cdot b \in S$ whenever $a, b \in S$   (closed under multiplication).

EXAMPLE 3–9. Every ring $(R, +, \cdot)$ has two trivial or improper subrings. For, if 0 denotes the zero element of the ring $(R, +, \cdot)$, then both $(\{0\}, +, \cdot)$ and $(R, +, \cdot)$ are subrings of $(R, +, \cdot)$.

EXAMPLE 3–10. In the ring of integers $(Z, +, \cdot)$, the triple $(Z_e, +, \cdot)$ is a subring, while $(Z_o, +, \cdot)$ is not. In particular, we infer that in a ring with identity, a subring need not contain the identity element.

EXAMPLE 3–11. Consider $(Z_6, +_6, \cdot_6)$, the ring of integers modulo 6. If $S = \{0, 2, 4\}$, then $(S, +_6, \cdot_6)$, whose operation tables are given below, is a subring of $(Z_6, +_6, \cdot_6)$.

| $+_6$ | 0 | 2 | 4 |
|-------|---|---|---|
| 0 | 0 | 2 | 4 |
| 2 | 2 | 4 | 0 |
| 4 | 4 | 0 | 2 |

| $\cdot_6$ | 0 | 2 | 4 |
|-----------|---|---|---|
| 0 | 0 | 0 | 0 |
| 2 | 0 | 4 | 2 |
| 4 | 0 | 2 | 4 |

EXAMPLE 3–12. Let $S = \{a + b\sqrt{3} \mid a, b \in Z\}$. Then $(S, +, \cdot)$ is a subring of $(R^{\#}, +, \cdot)$, since for $a, b, c, d \in Z$

$$(a + b\sqrt{3}) - (c + d\sqrt{3}) = (a - c) + (b - d)\sqrt{3} \in S,$$

$$(a + b\sqrt{3}) \cdot (c + d\sqrt{3}) = (ac + 3bd) + (bc + ad)\sqrt{3} \in S.$$

This shows that $S$ is closed under both differences and products.

An operation-preserving function between two rings $(R_1, +, \cdot)$ and $(R_2, *, \circ)$, as one might expect, is a function $f: R_1 \to R_2$ which preserves both ring operations. We need merely apply the familiar operation-preserving concept to the additive groups $(R_1, +)$ and $(R_2, *)$, and to the multiplicative semigroups $(R_1, \cdot)$ and $(R_2, \circ)$. More formally, we state the following definition.

> **DEFINITION 3–9.** Let $(R_1, +, \cdot)$ and $(R_2, *, \circ)$ be two rings and $f$ a function from $R_1$ into $R_2$, $f: R_1 \to R_2$. Then $f$ is said to be an *operation-preserving function* (or *ring homomorphism*) *from* $(R_1, +, \cdot)$ *into* $(R_2, *, \circ)$ if and only if
>
> $f(a + b) = f(a) * f(b),$
>
> $f(a \cdot b) = f(a) \circ f(b),$
>
> for each pair of elements $a, b \in R_1$.
> If, in addition, $f$ is a one-to-one mapping onto $R_2$ [that is, $f(R_1) = R_2$], then the rings $(R_1, +, \cdot)$ and $(R_2, *, \circ)$ are *algebraically equivalent*.

EXAMPLE 3–13. Let $(R_1, +, \cdot)$ and $(R_2, *, \circ)$ be arbitrary rings and let $f: R_1 \to R_2$ be the function that takes each element of $R_1$ into the zero element $\bar{0}$ of $(R_2, *, \circ)$. Such a mapping is operation-preserving, for

$$f(a + b) = \bar{0} = \bar{0} * \bar{0} = f(a) * f(b),$$

$$f(a \cdot b) = \bar{0} = \bar{0} \circ \bar{0} = f(a) \circ f(b).$$

EXAMPLE 3–14.  Consider $(Z, +, \cdot)$, the ring of integers, and $(Z_n, +_n, \cdot_n)$, the ring of integers modulo $n$.  Define $f: Z \to Z_n$ by $f(a) = [a]$; that is, map each integer into the congruence class containing it.  Then

$$f(a + b) = [a + b] = [a] +_n [b] = f(a) +_n f(b),$$
$$f(a \cdot b) = [a \cdot b] = [a] \cdot_n [b] = f(a) \cdot_n f(b),$$

so that $f$ is operation-preserving.

EXAMPLE 3–15.  The mapping $f: Z \to Z_e$ defined by $f(a) = 2a$ is not an operation-preserving function from $(Z, +, \cdot)$ into $(Z_e, +, \cdot)$.  For while addition is preserved, multiplication is not:

$$f(a + b) = 2(a + b) = 2a + 2b = f(a) + f(b);$$
but
$$f(a \cdot b) = 2(a \cdot b) \neq (2a) \cdot (2b) = f(a) \cdot f(b).$$

EXAMPLE 3–16.  In Example 3–7, the system $(R^\# \times R^\#, +, \cdot)$ was shown to be a ring if addition and multiplication were defined by the rules

$$(a, b) + (c, d) = (a + c, b + d), \qquad (a, b) \cdot (c, d) = (ac, bd).$$

The reader may check that if

$$S = \{(a, a) \mid a \in R^\#\},$$

then $(S, +, \cdot)$ is a subring of $(R^\# \times R^\#, +, \cdot)$.  This subring is algebraically equivalent to $(R^\#, +, \cdot)$ under the mapping $f: S \to R^\#$ defined by

$$f[(a, a)] = a.$$

If $f$ is an operation-preserving function from the ring $(R_1, +, \cdot)$ into the ring $(R_2, *, \circ)$, then the *kernel* of $f$ is the set

$$\ker(f) = \{a \in R_1 \mid f(a) = \overline{0}\},$$

where $\overline{0}$ is the zero element of $(R_2, *, \circ)$.  If we were to ignore the multiplication operations in the rings $(R_1, +, \cdot)$ and $(R_2, *, \circ)$, this becomes just the usual definition of the kernel of an operation-preserving function between the groups $(R_1, +)$ and $(R_2, *)$.

The next theorem gives the ring-theoretic analogues of Theorems 2–19, 2–20, and 2–21.  We shall omit the proofs of these statements, since they are closely parallel to those of the corresponding results for groups.  The parts of the theorem concerning addition carry over with only a change in notation.

**THEOREM 3–5.** Let $f$ be an operation-preserving function from the ring $(R_1, +, \cdot)$ into the ring $(R_2, *, \circ)$. Then the following statements hold:

(1) $f(0) = \bar{0}$, where $\bar{0}$ is the zero element of $(R_2, *, \circ)$;
(2) $f(-a) = -f(a)$;
(3) $(\ker(f), +, \cdot)$ is a subring of $(R_1, +, \cdot)$;
(4) $(f(R_1), *, \circ)$ is a subring of $(R_2, *, \circ)$;
(5) $f$ is one-to-one if and only if $\ker(f) = \{0\}$.

If, in addition, $(R_1, +, \cdot)$ and $(R_2, *, \circ)$ are rings with identity elements 1 and $\bar{1}$, respectively, and $f(R_1) = R_2$, then

(6) $f(1) = \bar{1}$;
(7) $f(a^{-1}) = f(a)^{-1}$ whenever $a^{-1}$ exists in $R_1$.

The first part of Theorem 3–5 indicates that $\ker(f)$ is a nonempty subset of $R_1$ for $0 \in \ker(f)$. In addition, we infer from (2) that

$$f(a - b) = f(a + (-b))$$
$$= f(a) * f(-b) = f(a) - f(b).$$

That is, an operation-preserving function preserves differences as well as sums and products. We shall need this fact presently.

We next introduce an important class of subrings, known as ideals, whose role in ring theory is similar to that of the distinguished subgroups in the study of groups. As we shall see, ideals lead to the construction of quotient rings which are the appropriate analogue of quotient groups.

**DEFINITION 3–10.** A subring $(I, +, \cdot)$ of the ring $(R, +, \cdot)$ is an *ideal* of $(R, +, \cdot)$ if and only if $r \in R$ and $a \in I$ imply both $r \cdot a \in I$ and $a \cdot r \in I$.

Thus we require that whenever one of the factors in a product belongs to $I$, the product itself must be a member of $I$. In a sense, the set $I$ "captures" products.

If $(I, +, \cdot)$ is a subring of $(R, +, \cdot)$, $I$ is already closed under multiplication. For $(I, +, \cdot)$ to be an ideal, a stronger closure condition is imposed: $I$ is closed under multiplication by an arbitrary element of $R$.

In view of Definition 3–8, which gives a minimum set of conditions on $I$ for $(I, +, \cdot)$ to be a subring, our present definition of ideal may be rephrased as follows.

**DEFINITION 3–11.** Let $(R, +, \cdot)$ be a ring and $I$ a nonempty subset of $R$. Then $(I, +, \cdot)$ is an ideal of $(R, +, \cdot)$ if and only if

(1) $a, b \in I$ implies $a - b \in I$,

(2) $r \in R$ and $a \in I$ imply both $r \cdot a \in I$ and $a \cdot r \in I$.

In the case of a commutative ring, of course, we need only require $r \cdot a \in I$.

Before proceeding further, we shall examine this concept by means of several specific examples.

EXAMPLE 3–17. In any ring $(R, +, \cdot)$, the improper subrings $(R, +, \cdot)$ and $(\{0\}, +, \cdot)$ are ideals.

EXAMPLE 3–18. The subring $(Z_e, +, \cdot)$ of even integers is an ideal of $(Z, +, \cdot)$.

EXAMPLE 3–19. For a given integer $a \in Z$, let $(a)$ denote the set of all integral multiples of $a$:

$$(a) = \{na \mid n \in Z\}.$$

As the following argument will show, $((a), +, \cdot)$ is an ideal of the ring $(Z, +, \cdot)$, called the *principal ideal generated by* $a$. If $na, ma \in (a)$ and $k \in Z$, then

$$na - ma = (n - m)a \in (a),$$

while

$$k(na) = (kn)a \in (a).$$

A generalization of this example is given as an exercise at the end of the section.

EXAMPLE 3–20. Suppose $(R, +, \cdot)$ is the commutative ring of functions of Example 3–4. Define

$$I = \{f \in R \mid f(1) = 0\}.$$

For functions $f, g \in I$ and $h \in R$, we have

$$(f - g)(1) = f(1) - g(1) = 0 - 0 = 0$$

and also

$$(h \cdot f)(1) = h(1) \cdot f(1) = h(1) \cdot 0 = 0.$$

Since both $f - g$ and $h \cdot g$ belong to $I$, $(I, +, \cdot)$ is an ideal of $(R, +, \cdot)$.

Actually, the principal ideals (see Example 3–19) are the only ideals of the ring of integers, as the following theorem will show.

> **THEOREM 3–6.** The ideals of the ring $(Z, +, \cdot)$ are the principal ideals $((a), +, \cdot)$, where $a \in Z_+$.

*Proof.* Since $Z = (1)$ and $\{0\} = (0)$, the improper ideals $(Z, +, \cdot)$ and $(\{0\}, +, \cdot)$ are both principal ideals. Suppose that $(I, +, \cdot)$ is any proper ideal of $(Z, +, \cdot)$ and let $a$ be the least positive integer in $I$. Then, $(I, +, \cdot)$ being an ideal, $I$ contains every element $na$ of $(a)$; that is, $(a) \subseteq I$. If the integer $k \in I$, then we may write $k = q \cdot a + r$, where $q, r \in Z$ and $0 \leq r < a$. But $q \cdot a$ and $k$ are in $I$, so that $k - q \cdot a = r \in I$. Our definition of the element $a$ implies $r = 0$, and consequently $k = q \cdot a$. Thus every element of $I$ is a member of $(a)$; that is, $I \subseteq (a)$. The two inclusions show that $I = (a)$, completing the argument.

We shall now develop several interesting and useful results concerning ideals of arbitrary rings.

> **THEOREM 3–7.** If $(I_1, +, \cdot)$ and $(I_2, +, \cdot)$ are ideals of the ring $(R, +, \cdot)$, then so also is $(I_1 \cap I_2, +, \cdot)$.

*Proof.* The set $I_1 \cap I_2 \neq \emptyset$, for $I_1$ and $I_2$ both contain the zero element of the ring. Suppose that the elements $a, b \in I_1 \cap I_2$ and $r \in R$. We first verify that the set $I_1 \cap I_2$ is closed under differences. Since $(I_1, +, \cdot)$ and $(I_2, +, \cdot)$ are both ideals of $(R, +, \cdot)$, we have $a - b \in I_1$ and $a - b \in I_2$. That is, $a - b \in I_1 \cap I_2$. Again the fact that $(I_1, +, \cdot)$ and $(I_2, +, \cdot)$ are ideals implies that $r \cdot a \in I_1$ and also $r \cdot a \in I_2$, making it an element of $I_1 \cap I_2$. Similar reasoning shows that $a \cdot r \in I_1 \cap I_2$, which completes the proof.

As a simple illustration, let $((2), +, \cdot)$ and $((3), +, \cdot)$ be the principal ideals generated by the integers 2 and 3 in the ring $(Z, +, \cdot)$. Then

$$((2) \cap (3), +, \cdot) = ((6), +, \cdot),$$

which is the principal ideal generated by 6.

If our analogy between ideals and distinguished subgroups is to be meaningful, we must anticipate that the kernel of an operation-preserving function between rings is an ideal. This is indeed the content of the following theorem.

> **THEOREM 3–8.** If $f$ is an operation-preserving function from the ring $(R_1, +, \cdot)$ into the ring $(R_2, *, \circ)$, then the system $(\ker(f), +, \cdot)$ is an ideal of $(R_1, +, \cdot)$.

*Proof.* As observed earlier, $0 \in \ker(f)$, so that the kernel is nonempty. Consider any two elements $a$ and $b$ of $\ker(f)$. We have $f(a) = \bar{0} = f(b)$, where $\bar{0}$ is the zero element of the ring $(R_2, *, \circ)$. Since any operation-preserving function between rings preserves differences, it follows that

$$f(a - b) = f(a) - f(b) = \bar{0} - \bar{0} = \bar{0},$$

and consequently $a - b \in \ker(f)$. Now, if $r$ is an arbitrary member of $R_1$, then

$$f(r \cdot a) = f(r) \circ f(a) = f(r) \circ \bar{0} = \bar{0}.$$

That is, $r \cdot a \in \ker(f)$. In a like manner, we conclude that $a \cdot r \in \ker(f)$. Accordingly $(\ker(f), +, \cdot)$ is an ideal of $(R_1, +, \cdot)$.

EXAMPLE 3–21. To illustrate this last theorem, let us consider the two rings $(Z, +, \cdot)$ and $(Z_n, +_n, \cdot_n)$, and the mapping $f : Z \to Z_n$ defined by

$$f(a) = [a].$$

It has been established previously that $f$ is operation-preserving (see Example 3–14). Here,

$$\begin{aligned}
\ker(f) &= \{a \in Z \mid f(a) = [0]\} \\
&= \{a \in Z \mid a = kn \text{ for some } k \in Z\} \\
&= (n).
\end{aligned}$$

In other words, $(\ker(f), +, \cdot)$ is just the principal ideal generated by the integer $n$.

We shall continue our discussion of ideals by presenting a result that will be useful in the next section on fields.

**THEOREM 3–9.** If $(I, +, \cdot)$ is a proper ideal of a ring $(R, +, \cdot)$ with identity, then no element of $I$ has a multiplicative inverse.

*Proof.* Suppose to the contrary that there is some member $a \neq 0$ of $I$ such that $a^{-1}$ exists. Since $I$ is closed under multiplication by arbitrary elements of $R$, $a^{-1} \cdot a = 1 \in I$. It then follows by the same reasoning that $I$ contains $r \cdot 1 = r$ for every $r \in I$. That is, $R \subseteq I$. Inasmuch as the opposite inclusion always holds, $I = R$, contradicting the hypothesis that $I$ is a proper subset of $R$.

We now turn our attention briefly to the matter of cosets in a ring. If $(I, +, \cdot)$ is an ideal of the ring $(R, +, \cdot)$, then, since addition is commutative, the system $(I, +)$ is a distinguished subgroup of $(R, +)$. Thus by the results of Section 2–4, we may construct the quotient group of $R$ by $I$.

In our present notation, the cosets of $I$ in $R$ are of the form

$$a + I = \{a + i \mid i \in I\},$$

where $a \in R$. By Theorem 2–14, two cosets $a + I$ and $b + I$ are equal if and only if $a - b \in I$.

As before, the collection of distinct cosets of $I$ in $R$ shall be denoted by $R/I$. It follows from Theorem 2–18 and Problem 16 (p. 51) that if addition of cosets is defined by the rule

$$(a + I) + (b + I) = (a + b) + I,$$

then $(R/I, +)$ becomes a commutative group. An operation of multiplication can also be introduced in $R/I$ in a natural way with the result that a ring is obtained; all we need to do is to specify

$$(a + I) \cdot (b + I) = (a \cdot b) + I.$$

Because $(I, +, \cdot)$ is an ideal, this definition of coset multiplication is well-defined and does not depend on the particular representatives of the cosets used. Indeed, suppose that

$$a + I = a' + I$$

and

$$b + I = b' + I.$$

Then, as observed above, $a - a' = i_1$ and $b - b' = i_2$, where $i_1, i_2 \in I$. From this, we conclude that

$$a \cdot b - a' \cdot b' = a \cdot (b - b') + (a - a') \cdot b'$$
$$= a \cdot i_2 + i_1 \cdot b' \in I,$$

since both the products $a \cdot i_1$ and $i_2 \cdot b'$ are in $I$. Consequently,

$$a \cdot b + I = a' \cdot b' + I.$$

The closure of $I$ under multiplication by arbitrary elements of $R$ thus leads to a meaningful definition of coset multiplication; indeed this is the principal reason for defining an ideal as we did.

> **THEOREM 3–10.** If $(I, +, \cdot)$ is an ideal of the ring $(R, +, \cdot)$, then the system $(R/I, +, \cdot)$ is a ring, known as the *quotient ring* of $R$ by $I$.

We omit the details of the proof and merely point out that the zero element of $(R/I, +, \cdot)$ is the coset $0 + I = I$, while $-(a + I) = (-a) + I$.

EXAMPLE 3–22. Consider the principal ideal $((n), +, \cdot)$ in the ring of integers $(Z, +, \cdot)$. The cosets of $(n)$ in $Z$ take the form

$$a + (n) = \{a + kn \mid k \in Z\} = [a],$$

i.e., the cosets are precisely the congruence classes modulo $n$: $Z/(n) = Z_n$. It follows from the definition of coset addition and multiplication that the quotient ring of $Z$ by $(n)$ is merely the ring of integers modulo $n$.

# PROBLEMS

1. Prove that the system $(\{0, 3, 6, 9\}, +_{12}, \cdot_{12})$ is a subring of $(Z_{12}, +_{12}, \cdot_{12})$, the ring of integers modulo 12.

2. Show that in a ring with identity, no divisor of zero can have a multiplicative inverse.

3. The *center* of a ring $(R, +, \cdot)$, denoted by cent $R$, is the set

   $$\text{cent } R = \{c \in R \mid c \cdot x = x \cdot c \text{ for all } x \in R\}.$$

   Prove that (cent $R, +, \cdot$) is a subring of $(R, +, \cdot)$.

4. Consider the ring $(R, +, \cdot)$, where

   $$R = \{a + b\sqrt{3} \mid a, b \in Z\}.$$

   (a) Show that the mapping $f: R \to R$, defined by

   $$f(a + b\sqrt{3}) = a - b\sqrt{3},$$

   is operation-preserving.
   (b) Is the function $f$, given by $f(a + b\sqrt{3}) = a$, an operation-preserving function from $(R, +, \cdot)$ into $(Z, +, \cdot)$?

5. Let $(R, +, \cdot)$ be an arbitrary ring and define the set $S$ by $S = R \times Z$:

   $$S = \{(a, n) \mid a \in R, n \in Z\}.$$

   Introduce two binary operations $*$ and $\circ$ on $S$ by the rules

   $$(a, n) * (b, m) = (a + b, n + m),$$
   $$(a, n) \circ (b, m) = (a \cdot b + nb + ma, nm).$$

   (a) Show that $(S, *, \circ)$ is a ring with identity element $(0, 1)$.
   (b) Given $S_1 = \{(a, 0) \mid a \in R\}$, prove that the rings $(S_1, *, \circ)$ and $(R, +, \cdot)$ are algebraically equivalent under the mapping $f: S_1 \to R$, where $f[(a, 0)] = a$. This shows that *any ring without identity can always be considered to be a subring of a ring with identity.*

6. Let $f$ be an operation-preserving function from the ring $(R, +, \cdot)$ into itself and let $S$ denote the set of elements of $R$ that are left fixed by $f$:

$$S = \{a \in R \mid f(a) = a\}.$$

Prove that $(S, +, \cdot)$ is a subring of $(R, +, \cdot)$.

7. Determine whether the system $(\{0, 3, 6\}, +_9, \cdot_9)$ is an ideal of the ring $(Z_9, +_9, \cdot_9)$.

8. Given $(I_1, +, \cdot)$ and $(I_2, +, \cdot)$ are ideals of the ring $(R, +, \cdot)$, let

$$I_1 + I_2 = \{a + b \mid a \in I_1, b \in I_2\}.$$

Show that $(I_1 + I_2, +, \cdot)$ is also an ideal of $(R, +, \cdot)$.

9. Suppose that $(R, +, \cdot)$ is a commutative ring with identity and $a \in R$. Define the set $(a)$ by

$$(a) = \{r \cdot a \mid r \in R\}.$$

Prove that $((a), +, \cdot)$ is an ideal of $(R, +, \cdot)$ containing the element $a$, known as the *principal ideal generated by* $a$. Observe that whenever $a$ has a multiplicative inverse, the principal ideal generated by $a$ is $(R, +, \cdot)$; on the other hand, if no such inverse exists, $((a), +, \cdot)$ is always a proper ideal.

10. Show by example that if $(I_1, +, \cdot)$ and $(I_2, +, \cdot)$ are both ideals of the ring $(R, +, \cdot)$, then $(I_1 \cup I_2, +, \cdot)$ is not necessarily an ideal.

11. Given $(R, +, \cdot)$ is a commutative ring and $a \in R$, let

$$I = \{x \in R \mid x \cdot a = 0\}.$$

Prove that $(I, +, \cdot)$ is an ideal of $(R, +, \cdot)$.

12. Let $(R, +, \cdot)$ be a ring with the property that $a^2 + a \in \text{cent } R$ for every element $a$ in $R$. Show that $(R, +, \cdot)$ is commutative. [*Hint:* Use the expression $(a + b)^2 + (a + b)$ to prove first that $a \cdot b + b \cdot a$ lies in cent $R$.]

13. Given $(I_1, +, \cdot)$ and $(I_2, +, \cdot)$ are ideals of the ring $(R, +, \cdot)$ such that $I_1 \cap I_2 = \{0\}$, prove that $a \cdot b = 0$ for every $a \in I_1, b \in I_2$.

14. Suppose that $(I, +, \cdot)$ is an ideal of the ring $(R, +, \cdot)$. Prove the following:
  (a) If $(R, +, \cdot)$ is commutative, then the quotient ring $(R/I, +, \cdot)$ is commutative.
  (b) The *natural mapping* $f: R \to R/I$, defined by $f(a) = a + I$, is an operation-preserving function.

15. Let $f$ be an operation-preserving function from the ring $(R_1, +, \cdot)$ into the ring $(R_2, *, \circ)$. Given that $a \in R_1$ is nilpotent, show that its image $f(a)$ is also nilpotent.

16. An ideal $(I, +, \cdot)$ of a commutative ring $(R, +, \cdot)$ is said to be *prime* if $a \cdot b \in I$ implies either $a \in I$ or $b \in I$. Prove that $(I, +, \cdot)$ is a prime ideal if and only if the quotient ring $(R/I, +, \cdot)$ is an integral domain.

## 3–3.  FIELDS

If $(R, +, \cdot)$ is a commutative ring with identity, and $G$ denotes the set of elements of $R$ having multiplicative inverses, then the pair $(G, \cdot)$ is a group (see Problem 6, p. 73). The set $G$ always contains the elements 1 and $-1$, but these may be its only members as, for example, is the case in the ring $(Z, +, \cdot)$. In order to study abstract systems whose algebraic structure closely parallels that of the real number system, we now restrict our attention to rings in which every nonzero element belongs to $G$. This leads to the notion of a field.

> **DEFINITION 3–12.** A *field* is a mathematical system $(F, +, \cdot)$, consisting of a nonempty set $F$ and two binary operations $+$ and $\cdot$ on $F$, called *addition* and *multiplication*, such that
>
> (1)  $(F, +)$ is a commutative group, with identity 0;
> (2)  $(F - \{0\}, \cdot)$ is a commutative group, with identity 1;
> (3)  for each triple of elements $a, b, c \in F$,
>
> $$a \cdot (b + c) = a \cdot b + a \cdot c.$$

In brief then, a field is a commutative ring with identity in which each nonzero element has an inverse under multiplication. Thus all the results of the preceding two sections on rings hold for our new system. For instance, by Theorem 3–1, we know that $a \cdot 0 = 0 = 0 \cdot a$ for any $a \in F$. This shows that all the elements of $F$ commute under multiplication and not merely the nonzero elements.

To distinguish the two inverses of a nonzero element of $a \in F$, we shall denote the inverse of $a$ relative to multiplication by $a^{-1}$ and retain the notation $-a$ for its inverse under the operation of addition. Observe that if the zero element itself were to possess a multiplicative inverse, then

$$0 = 0 \cdot a = 1$$

for some $a \in F$. By Theorem 3–4, the condition $0 = 1$ implies $F = \{0\}$, contradicting our assumption that all rings considered contain more than one element.

EXAMPLE 3–23.  Both the systems $(R^{\#}, +, \cdot)$ and $(Q, +, \cdot)$, where $+$ and $\cdot$ indicate ordinary addition and multiplication, are fields.

EXAMPLE 3–24.  The ring $(R_U, *, \cap)$ of subsets of a nonempty universe $U$ considered in Example 3–3 is not a field, for the pair $(R_U - \{\emptyset\}, \cap)$ fails to be a group.

EXAMPLE 3–25.  Let $F$ be the set of real numbers of the form $a + b\sqrt{3}$, with $a$ and $b$ rational:

$$F = \{a + b\sqrt{3} \mid a, b \in Q\}.$$

It is straightforward to check that the triple $(F, +, \cdot)$ is a commutative ring with identity (see Example 3–5).  The additive and multiplicative identity elements in this case are

$$0 = 0 + 0\sqrt{3}, \qquad 1 = 1 + 0\sqrt{3}.$$

To show that $(F, +, \cdot)$ is a field, we must verify that each nonzero element of $F$ has an inverse belonging to $F$.  Suppose then that $a + b\sqrt{3} \in F$, where $a$ and $b$ are not both zero.  Under these circumstances, $a^2 - 3b^2 \neq 0$, for otherwise $\sqrt{3}$ would be rational.  This means that

$$(a + b\sqrt{3})^{-1} = \frac{1}{a + b\sqrt{3}} = \frac{1}{a + b\sqrt{3}} \frac{a - b\sqrt{3}}{a - b\sqrt{3}}$$

$$= \frac{a}{a^2 - 3b^2} + \frac{-b}{a^2 - 3b^2} \sqrt{3} \in F.$$

Since $a/(a^2 - 3b^2)$ and $-b/(a^2 - 3b^2)$ are both rational numbers, the resulting inverse does have the required form to be a member of $F$.

Note that if $a$ and $b$ were restricted simply to being integers, then $(F, +, \cdot)$ would no longer be a field, for then the element

$$\frac{a}{a^2 - 3b^2} + \frac{-b}{a^2 - 3b^2} \sqrt{3}$$

would not necessarily be in $F$.

EXAMPLE 3–26.  Consider the set $C = R^{\#} \times R^{\#}$ of ordered pairs of real numbers.  Define addition and multiplication in $C$ by the formulas

$$(a, b) + (c, d) = (a + c, b + d),$$
$$(a, b) \cdot (c, d) = (ac - bd, ad + bc).$$

It is not difficult to verify that $(C, +, \cdot)$ is a commutative ring with identity element $(1, 0)$.  Here the zero element of the ring is the pair $(0, 0)$.  If $(a, b) \neq (0, 0)$, then

$$(a, b)^{-1} = \left( \frac{a}{a^2 + b^2}, \frac{-b}{a^2 + b^2} \right),$$

since

$$(a, b) \cdot \left( \frac{a}{a^2 + b^2}, \frac{-b}{a^2 + b^2} \right) = \left( \frac{a^2 + b^2}{a^2 + b^2}, \frac{-ab + ab}{a^2 + b^2} \right) = (1, 0).$$

That is, each nonzero element of $C$ has a multiplicative inverse. This proves that the system $(C, +, \cdot)$ is a field.

It follows from the definition of the operations $+$ and $\cdot$ that any element $(a, b) \in C$ may be expressed in the form

$$(a, b) = (a, 0) + (b, 0) \cdot (0, 1),$$

where $(0, 1)^2 = (0, 1) \cdot (0, 1) = (-1, 0)$. Introducing the customary symbol $i$ for the pair $(0, 1)$, we have

$$(a, b) = (a, 0) + (b, 0) \cdot i.$$

If it is agreed to replace a pair of the form $(a, 0)$ by its first component $a$, then each member of $C$ has the representation

$$(a, b) = a + bi,$$

where $i^2 = -1$. In other words, the field $(C, +, \cdot)$ is just the usual complex number system.

The following theorem shows that a field is without divisors of zero, and consequently is a system in which the cancellation law for multiplication holds (see Theorem 3–3).

**THEOREM 3–11.** If $(F, +, \cdot)$ is a field and $a, b \in F$ with $a \cdot b = 0$, then either $a = 0$ or $b = 0$.

*Proof.* If $a = 0$, the theorem is already established. So let us suppose that $a \neq 0$ and prove that $b = 0$. By the definition of a field the element $a$, being nonzero, must have a multiplicative inverse $a^{-1} \in F$. The hypothesis $a \cdot b = 0$ then yields

$$0 = a^{-1} \cdot 0 = a^{-1} \cdot (a \cdot b) = (a^{-1} \cdot a) \cdot b = 1 \cdot b = b,$$

as desired.

Since a field is a commutative ring with identity, and we have just proved that it contains no divisors of zero, we conclude that any field is an integral domain. There are obviously integral domains which are not fields; for instance, the ring of integers.

It was seen previously that for each positive integer $n$ the system $(Z_n, +_n, \cdot_n)$ is a commutative ring with identity. Our next result indicates precisely for what values of $n$ this ring is actually a field.

**THEOREM 3–12.** The ring $(Z_n, +_n, \cdot_n)$ of integers modulo $n$ is a field if and only if $n$ is a prime number.

*Proof.* We first show that if $n$ is not prime, then $(Z_n, +_n, \cdot_n)$ is not a field. Thus assume $n = a \cdot b$, where $0 < a < n$ and $0 < b < n$. It follows at once that

$$[a] \cdot_n [b] = [a \cdot b] = [n] = [0],$$

although both $[a] \neq [0]$, $[b] \neq [0]$. This means the system $(Z_n, +_n, \cdot_n)$ is not an integral domain, and hence not a field.

On the other hand, suppose that $n$ is a prime number. To show that $(Z_n, +_n, \cdot_n)$ is a field, it suffices to prove here that each nonzero element of $Z_n$ has a multiplicative inverse in $Z_n$. To this end, let $[a] \in Z_n$, where $0 < a < n$. According to a well-known result from number theory, since $a$ and $n$ have no common factors, there exist integers $r$ and $s$ such that

$$a \cdot r + n \cdot s = 1.$$

This implies that

$$
\begin{aligned}
[a] \cdot_n [r] &= [a \cdot r] +_n [0] = [a \cdot r] +_n [n \cdot s] \\
&= [a \cdot r + n \cdot s] \\
&= [1],
\end{aligned}
$$

showing the congruence class $[r]$ to be the multiplicative inverse of $[a]$. Therefore $(Z_n, +_n, \cdot_n)$ is a field as required.

There is an interesting relationship between fields and their ideals, or rather their lack of ideals.

> **THEOREM 3-13.** Let $(R, +, \cdot)$ be a commutative ring with identity. Then $(R, +, \cdot)$ is a field if and only if $(R, +, \cdot)$ has no proper ideals.

*Proof.* Suppose first that $(R, +, \cdot)$ is a field. We wish to show that the improper ideals $(\{0\}, +, \cdot)$ and $(R, +, \cdot)$ are its only ideals. Let us assume to the contrary that there exists some nontrivial ideal $(I, +, \cdot)$ of $(R, +, \cdot)$. By our assumption, the subset $I$ is such that $I \neq \{0\}$ and $I \neq R$. This means there is some nonzero element $a \in I$. Since $(R, +, \cdot)$ is a field, $a$ has a multiplicative inverse $a^{-1} \in R$. By the definition of ideal, we thus obtain $a^{-1} \cdot a = 1 \in I$, which in turn implies $I = R$, contradicting our choice of $I$.

Conversely, suppose that the ring $(R, +, \cdot)$ has no proper ideals. For an arbitrary nonzero element $a \in R$, consider the set

$$I_a = \{a \cdot r \mid r \in R\}$$

of right multiples of $a$ by elements of $R$. One can readily verify that the triple $(I_a, +, \cdot)$ is an ideal of $(R, +, \cdot)$ (see Problem 9, p. 83) and cannot be the zero ideal, since $a \cdot 1 = a \in I_a$, where $a \neq 0$. It follows from the hypothesis that the only other possibility is $(I_a, +, \cdot) = (R, +, \cdot)$; that is, $I_a = R$. In particular, since $1 \in I_a$, there is an element $b \in R$ such that $a \cdot b = 1$. To complete the proof, it suffices to recall that multiplication is commutative, so that $b = a^{-1}$. Thus each nonzero element of $R$ has a multiplicative inverse.

In view of this last theorem, the ring of integers $(Z, +, \cdot)$ fails to be a field, since it has the proper ideal $(Z_e, +, \cdot)$.

The reader may have speculated on the result of replacing, in the field axioms, the distributivity of multiplication over addition by the distributivity of addition over multiplication. We conclude our study of systems with two operations by briefly investigating this situation.

**DEFINITION 3–13.** A b-*field*, or *backward field*, is a mathematical system $(F, +, \cdot)$ consisting of a nonempty set $F$ and two binary operations $+$ and $\cdot$ defined on $F$, such that

(1) $(F, +)$ is a commutative group, with identity 0;
(2) $(F - \{0\}, \cdot)$ is a group, with identity 1;
(3) $a \cdot b = b \cdot a$ for each pair of elements $a, b \in F$;
(4) for each triple of elements $a, b, c \in F$,

$$a + (b \cdot c) = (a + b) \cdot (a + c).$$

Our object is to show that there are no b-fields, other than the system $(\{0\}, +, \cdot)$, but first we require two preliminary lemmas.

**LEMMA 1.** In a b-field $(F, +, \cdot)$, if $a \in F$ with $a + 1 \neq 0$, then $a = 0$.

*Proof.* For any $a \in F$, the distributive law (4) implies

$$a + 1 = a + (1 \cdot 1) = (a + 1) \cdot (a + 1).$$

If the element $a + 1 \neq 0$, then by the cancellation law in the group $(F - \{0\}, \cdot)$, $a + 1 = 1$ and consequently $a = 0$.

**LEMMA 2.** In any b-field, the elements 0 and 1 are identical.

*Proof.* Either $1 + 1 = 0$ or $1 + 1 \neq 0$. If $1 + 1 = 0$, then using the distributivity of addition over multiplication, we have

$$1 + (1 \cdot 0) = (1 + 1) \cdot (1 + 0) = 0 \cdot 1 = 1 \cdot 0 = 0 + (1 \cdot 0),$$

from which it follows that $1 = 0$. On the other hand, if $1 + 1 \neq 0$, then Lemma 1 implies $1 = 0$. In any event, we obtain $1 = 0$.

Since $1 = 0$, one is tempted to invoke Theorem 3–4 and thus conclude that $F = \{0\}$. But the proof of this theorem depended on the discarded distributive law; so some other argument must be employed.

**THEOREM 3–14.** The only b-field is the system $(\{0\}, +, \cdot)$.

*Proof.* Suppose to the contrary that there exists a b-field $(F, +, \cdot)$ where $F - \{0\} \neq \emptyset$. Then there is some element $a \in F$ with $a \neq 0$. By Lemma 1, this means that $a + 1 = 0$. But $1 = 0$, so that $a + 0 = 0 = 0 + 0$. An application of the cancellation law for the group $(F, +)$ yields the contradiction $a = 0$. In other words, $F - \{0\} = \emptyset$ or $F = \{0\}$.

# PROBLEMS

1. For which of the following sets $F$ is $(F, +, \cdot)$ a field?
   (a) $F = \{a - b\sqrt{2} \mid a, b \in Z\}$
   (b) $F = \{a + b\sqrt[3]{2} \mid a, b \in Q\}$
   (c) $F = \{a + b\sqrt[3]{2} + c\sqrt[3]{4} \mid a, b, c \in Q\}$

2. In a field $(F, +, \cdot)$, show that $a^2 = a$ implies $a = 0$ or $a = 1$.

3. Prove that the system $(\{0, 1\}, +, \cdot)$ is a field if the operations $+$ and $\cdot$ are as given by the tables:

| + | 0 | 1 |
|---|---|---|
| 0 | 0 | 1 |
| 1 | 1 | 0 |

| · | 0 | 1 |
|---|---|---|
| 0 | 0 | 0 |
| 1 | 0 | 1 |

4. In the field $(C, +, \cdot)$ of complex numbers define the mapping $f \colon C \to C$ by the rule $f[(a, b)] = (a, -b)$: in other words,

$$f(a + bi) = a - bi.$$

Determine whether the function $f$ is operation-preserving.

5. Let $(F, +, \cdot)$ be a field and $S$ be a subset of $F$ containing at least two elements. Prove that the triple $(S, +, \cdot)$ is itself a field [that is, $(S, +, \cdot)$ is a *subfield* of $(F, +, \cdot)$] when
   (1) $a, b \in S$ implies $a - b \in S$,
   (2) $a, b \in S$ and $a \neq 0$ imply $a \cdot b^{-1} \in S$.

6. Consider the subset $S \subset R^{\#}$ defined by $S = \{a + b\sqrt{2} \mid a, b \in Q\}$. Show that $(S, +, \cdot)$ is a subfield of $(R^{\#}, +, \cdot)$.

7. Prove that any integral domain with a finite number of elements is a field. [*Hint:* Assume $a \neq 0$ and consider the set of elements $a, a^2, a^3, \ldots$]

8. Consider the set of numbers $F = \{a + b\sqrt{2} \mid a, b \in Z\}$. Show that the ring $(F, +, \cdot)$ is not a field by exhibiting a proper ideal of $(F, +, \cdot)$.

9. For each pair of elements $a, b \neq 0$ of a field $(F, +, \cdot)$, let $a/b = a \cdot b^{-1}$. In this manner, the notion of the *quotient of a by b* may be introduced. Prove the following elementary rules for quotients:

   (a) $a/1 = a; 1/b = b^{-1}; b/b = 1; 0/b = 0$
   (b) $c \cdot (a/b) = (c \cdot a)/b = a \cdot (c/b)$
   (c) $-(a/b) = -a/b = a/-b$

10. Let $(F, +, \cdot)$ be a field and $a, b, c, d \in F$ with $b$ and $d$ nonzero. Show that:

   (a) $(a/b) + (c/d) = (a \cdot d + b \cdot c)/b \cdot d$
   (b) $(a/b)(c/d) = a \cdot c/b \cdot d$
   (c) $(a/b)/(c/d) = a \cdot d/b \cdot c$

*Chapter 4*

# MATRIX THEORY:
# AN ALGEBRAIC VIEW

## 4-1. VECTORS AND MATRICES

The theory of matrices has long occupied a strategic position in various branches of mathematics, physics, and engineering. It is only in recent years that its importance in the social and biological sciences as well has become apparent. The subject today has become an indispensable tool in such new fields as game theory, linear programming, and statistical decision theory. Part of the reason for the widening applicability of matrix theory is no doubt the role it plays in the analysis of discrete observations and the ease with which matrix operations may be programmed for high-speed computers.

We do not intend to give a complete and systematic account of the problems of matrix theory and its diverse applications, though we shall present a brief discussion of the computational techniques required for solving two of the more basic problems: the inversion of a matrix and the solution of a system of linear equations. Rather, the operations and basic properties of vectors and matrices are approached from an algebraic point of view with the aim of illustrating the concepts of the previous chapters. One result of such a study will be the formulation of a mathematical system, somewhat more complicated than those studied earlier, known as a vector space.

**DEFINITION 4–1**  An $n$-component, or $n$-dimensional, *vector* is an $n$-tuple of real numbers written either in a row (row vector)

$$(x_1, x_2, \ldots, x_n)$$

or in a column (column vector)

$$\begin{pmatrix} x_1 \\ x_2 \\ \vdots \\ x_n \end{pmatrix}.$$

The numbers $x_k \in R^{\#}$ are called the *components* of the vector, and we say $n$ is the *dimension* of the vector. Clearly, a one-dimensional vector is just a real number. We will condense our notation and henceforth write $(x_k)$ for the vector whose components are the $x_k$'s.

Suppose $(x_k)$ and $(y_k)$ are two $n$-component vectors of the same type; that is, either both row vectors or both column vectors. Then $(x_k)$ and $(y_k)$ are said to be *equal*, in which case we write $(x_k) = (y_k)$, if and only if their corresponding components are equal:

$$(x_k) = (y_k) \qquad \text{if and only if} \qquad x_k = y_k$$

for

$$k = 1, 2, \ldots, n.$$

For instance, $(1, 2, 3, 4) \neq (1, 2, 5, 4)$, since their third components differ.

**DEFINITION 4–2**

(a) The *sum of the vectors $(x_k)$ and $(y_k)$*, denoted by $(x_k) + (y_k)$, is the vector obtained by adding their corresponding components. Thus

$$(x_k) + (y_k) = (x_k + y_k).$$

(b) The *product of the vector $(x_k)$ and the real number* $\lambda$, denoted by $\lambda(x_k)$, is the vector obtained by multiplying each component of $(x_k)$ by $\lambda$. Thus

$$\lambda(x_k) = (\lambda x_k).$$

While we have used the plus sign in two different contexts in the above definition, for vectors and for their components, this should be no cause for confusion. It is clear that the difference of two vectors may be expressed in terms of the operations already defined as

$$(x_k) - (y_k) = (x_k) + (-1)(y_k).$$

As an illustration of Definition 4–2, consider

$$\begin{pmatrix} 1 \\ 2 \\ 3 \end{pmatrix} - 2 \begin{pmatrix} 1 \\ 0 \\ -1 \end{pmatrix} = \begin{pmatrix} 1 \\ 2 \\ 3 \end{pmatrix} + \begin{pmatrix} -2 \\ 0 \\ 2 \end{pmatrix} = \begin{pmatrix} 1-2 \\ 2+0 \\ 3+2 \end{pmatrix} = \begin{pmatrix} -1 \\ 2 \\ 5 \end{pmatrix}.$$

**DEFINITION 4–3.** Any vector whose components are all zero is called a *zero vector* and is represented by the symbol *0*.

Let $V_n$ denote the set of all $n$-component vectors of a given type (row or column). Inasmuch as vector addition has the basic additive properties of its components, the following theorem concerning the algebraic nature of $(V_n, +)$ is quite obvious and we thus omit its proof.

**THEOREM 4–1.** The system $(V_n, +)$ is a commutative group, having the zero vector of dimension $n$ as its identity element, and $(-x_k)$ as the inverse of a vector $(x_k) \in V_n$.

The operation of multiplication of vectors by real numbers, defined above, has the following properties: If $\lambda, \mu \in R^{\#}$ and $(x_k)$, $(y_k)$ are elements of $V_n$, then

(1) $(\lambda + \mu)(x_k) = \lambda(x_k) + \mu(x_k)$;

(2) $\lambda[(x_k) + (y_k)] = \lambda(x_k) + \lambda(y_k)$;

(3) $\lambda[\mu(x_k)] = (\lambda\mu)(x_k)$, $1(x_k) = (x_k)$, $0(x_k) = 0$.

Verification of this is left to the reader, since it is not particularly difficult.

Vectors may also be combined under a rule of combination known as inner product multiplication.

**DEFINITION 4–4.** If $(x_k)$ and $(y_k)$ are an $n$-component row vector and an $n$-component column vector, respectively, then their *inner product* is symbolized by $(x_k) \cdot (y_k)$ and defined as

$$(x_k) \cdot (y_k) = (x_1, x_2, \ldots, x_n) \cdot \begin{pmatrix} y_1 \\ y_2 \\ \vdots \\ y_n \end{pmatrix}$$

$$= x_1 y_1 + x_2 y_2 + \cdots + x_n y_n.$$

Note that the inner product is not defined unless both vectors are of the same dimension, and we always have

(row vector) $\cdot$ (column vector) $=$ real number.

For example,

$$(1, 2, -3) \cdot \begin{pmatrix} 7 \\ 6 \\ 5 \end{pmatrix} = 1 \cdot 7 + 2 \cdot 6 + (-3) \cdot 5 = 4.$$

Using the sigma notation,

$$\sum_{k=1}^{n} a_k = a_1 + a_2 + \cdots + a_n,$$

we can express the definition more concisely as

$$(x_k) \cdot (y_k) = \sum_{k=1}^{n} x_k y_k.$$

It is quite possible for the inner product of two nonzero vectors to be zero, as is the case with

$$(1, 2) \cdot \begin{pmatrix} -4 \\ 2 \end{pmatrix} = 1 \cdot (-4) + 2 \cdot 2 = 0.$$

However, the reader should not jump to any hasty conclusions concerning divisors of zero, for on the right-hand side we have the real number zero and not a 2-component zero vector.

While failing to be a binary operation, inner product multiplication nevertheless possesses some useful properties, which are listed in the next theorem.

> **THEOREM 4-2.** If $\lambda \in R^{\#}$ and $(x_k)$, $(y_k)$, $(z_k)$ are $n$-component vectors for which the indicated operations are defined, then
>
> (1) $(x_k) \cdot [(y_k) + (z_k)] = (x_k) \cdot (y_k) + (x_k) \cdot (z_k),$
> (2) $[(y_k) + (z_k)] \cdot (x_k) = (y_k) \cdot (x_k) + (z_k) \cdot (x_k),$
> (3) $\lambda[(x_k) \cdot (y_k)] = (\lambda x_k) \cdot (y_k) = (x_k) \cdot (\lambda y_k),$
> (4) $0 \cdot (x_k) = 0 = (x_k) \cdot 0.$

*Proof.* We shall establish only the first statement and leave the remaining parts of the theorem as an exercise. In sigma notation,

$$(x_k) \cdot [(y_k) + (z_k)] = (x_k) \cdot (y_k + z_k)$$

$$= \sum_{k=1}^{n} x_k(y_k + z_k)$$

$$= \sum_{k=1}^{n} x_k y_k + \sum_{k=1}^{n} x_k y_k$$

$$= (x_k) \cdot (y_k) + (x_k) \cdot (z_k).$$

**DEFINITION 4–5.** An $m \times n$ *matrix* (plural: *matrices*) is a rectangular display of real numbers consisting of $m$ rows and $n$ columns, written in the form

$$\begin{pmatrix} a_{11} & a_{12} & \cdots & a_{1n} \\ a_{21} & a_{22} & \cdots & a_{2n} \\ \vdots & & & \vdots \\ a_{m1} & a_{m2} & \cdots & a_{mn} \end{pmatrix}.$$

Thus $\begin{pmatrix} 1 & 2 & 3 \\ 0 & 1 & -1 \end{pmatrix}$ is a $2 \times 3$ matrix, but something like $\begin{pmatrix} 1 & 4 \\ & 2 \\ 6 & 7 \end{pmatrix}$

is not a matrix. A matrix has no numerical value; it is merely a way of arranging numbers.

The real numbers which occur within the display are called the *elements* or *entries* of the matrix, while the integers $m$ and $n$ are referred to as its *dimensions*. Elements are located in the matrix by the use of double subscripts, the first subscript indicating the row and the second subscript the column in which the element is found. For instance, the element $a_{11}$ lies in the first row and first column (the upper left-hand corner), while $a_{23}$ is in the second row and third column.

To avoid cumbersome notations, it is convenient to abbreviate a matrix as $(a_{ij})_{m \times n}$, which means "the matrix of dimension $m \times n$ whose elements are the $a_{ij}$'s." When the numbers of rows and columns are clearly understood, we may instead simply write $(a_{ij})$. If $m = n$, the matrix is said to be *square* of order $n$.

**DEFINITION 4–6.** Two $m \times n$ matrices $(a_{ij})$ and $(b_{ij})$ are *equal*, for which we write $(a_{ij}) = (b_{ij})$, if and only if their corresponding elements are equal. That is, $a_{ij} = b_{ij}$ for all $i$ and $j$.

Since an $m \times n$ matrix may be regarded as a collection of $m$ row vectors, or alternatively as a collection of $n$ column vectors, it is not surprising that the operations defined in $V_n$ for vectors have natural generalizations to matrix operations. We are thus led to an algebraic theory of matrices.

**DEFINITION 4–7**

(a) The *sum of two $m \times n$ matrices* $(a_{ij})$ and $(b_{ij})$, denoted by $(a_{ij}) + (b_{ij})$, is the matrix obtained by adding their corresponding elements. Thus $(a_{ij}) + (b_{ij}) = (a_{ij} + b_{ij})$.

(b) The *product of the matrix $(a_{ij})$ and the real number* $\lambda$, denoted by $\lambda(a_{ij})$, is the matrix obtained by multiplying each element of $(a_{ij})$ by $\lambda$. Thus $\lambda(a_{ij}) = (\lambda a_{ij})$.

Observe that by its definition addition is a binary operation on the set of all matrices of a given size. That is, the sum of two $n \times m$ matrices is again an $n \times m$ matrix.

EXAMPLE 4-1. Let

$$A = \begin{pmatrix} 1 & -6 & 2 \\ 3 & 0 & 1 \end{pmatrix}, \qquad B = \begin{pmatrix} 3 & 4 & 5 \\ 2 & -1 & 2 \end{pmatrix}.$$

Then

$$2A + B = \begin{pmatrix} 2 & -12 & 4 \\ 6 & 0 & 2 \end{pmatrix} + \begin{pmatrix} 3 & 4 & 5 \\ 2 & -1 & 2 \end{pmatrix}$$

$$= \begin{pmatrix} 5 & -8 & 9 \\ 8 & -1 & 4 \end{pmatrix}.$$

A matrix each of whose elements is zero is called a *zero matrix* and denoted by *0*. Accordingly, a zero matrix need not be square. For the zero matrix whose dimensions are those of $(a_{ij})$, we have

$$(a_{ij}) + 0 = (a_{ij}) = 0 + (a_{ij}),$$
$$(a_{ij}) + (-1)(a_{ij}) = 0 = (-1)(a_{ij}) + (a_{ij}).$$

Let us denote the set of $m \times n$ matrices by the symbol $M_{m \times n}$. The following theorem establishes the algebraic properties of $M_{m \times n}$ under matrix addition.

**THEOREM 4-3.** The mathematical system $(M_{m \times n}, +)$ is a commutative group, with the $m \times n$ zero matrix as the identity element and $(-a_{ij})$ as the inverse of a matrix $(a_{ij}) \in M_{m \times n}$.

*Proof.* Definition 4-7 indicates that each property of matrix addition is derived from the corresponding property of real number addition. For instance, to establish the commutative law, let $(a_{ij}), (b_{ij}) \in M_{m \times n}$. Then

$$(a_{ij}) + (b_{ij}) = (a_{ij} + b_{ij}) = (b_{ij} + a_{ij}) = (b_{ij}) + (a_{ij}).$$

The remainder of the theorem is equally straightforward and its verification is left to the reader.

Although multiplication of elements in $M_{m \times n}$ by a real number is not a binary operation on $M_{m \times n}$ (unless $m = n = 1$), this operation has several interesting and useful properties. Specifically, if $(a_{ij})$ and $(b_{ij}) \in M_{m \times n}$, then for $\lambda, \mu \in R^{\#}$

$$\lambda[(a_{ij}) + (b_{ij})] = \lambda(a_{ij}) + \lambda(b_{ij}),$$
$$(\lambda\mu)(a_{ij}) = \lambda[\mu(a_{ij})],$$
$$(\lambda + \mu)(a_{ij}) = \lambda(a_{ij}) + \mu(a_{ij}),$$
$$1(a_{ij}) = (a_{ij}), \qquad 0(a_{ij}) = 0.$$

Our main purpose for introducing inner product multiplication for vectors becomes apparent with the following definition.

> **DEFINITION 4–8.** If $(a_{ij})$ is an $m \times n$ matrix and $(b_{ij})$ is an $n \times r$ matrix, then their *product* $(c_{ij}) = (a_{ij}) \cdot (b_{ij})$ is an $m \times r$ matrix whose elements are given by the formula
>
> $$c_{ij} = \sum_{k=1}^{n} a_{ik}b_{kj} \quad \text{for} \quad i = 1, 2, \ldots, m, \quad j = 1, 2, \ldots, r.$$

As the subscripts indicate, the $ij$th entry $c_{ij}$ in the product matrix $(a_{ij}) \cdot (b_{ij})$ is obtained by taking the inner product of the $i$th row of $(a_{ij})$ and the $j$th column of $(b_{ij})$:

$$c_{ij} = (a_{i1}, a_{i2}, \ldots, a_{in}) \cdot \begin{pmatrix} b_{1j} \\ b_{2j} \\ \vdots \\ b_{nj} \end{pmatrix}.$$

As we observed previously, the inner product of two vectors is defined only if the vectors involved have the same number of components. Thus for the matrix product $(a_{ij}) \cdot (b_{ij})$ to exist, the number of columns in the matrix $(a_{ij})$ [which determines the number of elements in a row of $(a_{ij})$] must be equal to the number of rows in the matrix $(b_{ij})$ [which determines the number of elements in a column of $(b_{ij})$]. This means that we could not, for example, multiply a $4 \times 3$ matrix and a $2 \times 3$ matrix.

Restricted to the set of square matrices of order $n$, matrix multiplication is a binary operation. For if $(a_{ij})$ and $(b_{ij})$ are both $n \times n$ matrices, then so is their product $(a_{ij}) \cdot (b_{ij})$.

It is perhaps worthwhile to consider an example in detail.

EXAMPLE 4–2. Let

$$A = \begin{pmatrix} 2 & 0 & 1 \\ 3 & 2 & -1 \end{pmatrix} \quad \text{and} \quad B = \begin{pmatrix} 3 & 1 \\ -1 & 0 \\ 0 & 2 \end{pmatrix}.$$

Then

$$A \cdot B = \underset{2 \times 3}{\begin{pmatrix} 2 & 0 & 1 \\ 3 & 2 & -1 \end{pmatrix}} \cdot \underset{3 \times 2}{\begin{pmatrix} 3 & 1 \\ -1 & 0 \\ 0 & 2 \end{pmatrix}}$$

$$= \underset{2 \times 2}{\begin{pmatrix} 2 \cdot 3 + 0 \cdot (-1) + 1 \cdot 0 & 2 \cdot 1 + 0 \cdot 0 + 1 \cdot 2 \\ 3 \cdot 3 + 2 \cdot (-1) + (-1) \cdot 0 & 3 \cdot 1 + 2 \cdot 0 + (-1) \cdot 2 \end{pmatrix}}$$

$$= \begin{pmatrix} 6 & 4 \\ 7 & 1 \end{pmatrix}.$$

On the other hand,

$$B \cdot A = \begin{pmatrix} 3 & 1 \\ -1 & 0 \\ 0 & 2 \end{pmatrix} \cdot \begin{pmatrix} 2 & 0 & 1 \\ 3 & 2 & -1 \end{pmatrix}$$

$$\qquad\qquad 3 \times 2 \qquad\qquad 2 \times 3$$

$$= \begin{pmatrix} 3 \cdot 2 + 1 \cdot 3 & 3 \cdot 0 + 1 \cdot 2 & 3 \cdot 1 + 1 \cdot (-1) \\ -1 \cdot 2 + 0 \cdot 3 & -1 \cdot 0 + 0 \cdot 2 & -1 \cdot 1 + 0 \cdot (-1) \\ 0 \cdot 2 + 2 \cdot 3 & 0 \cdot 0 + 2 \cdot 2 & 0 \cdot 1 + 2 \cdot (-1) \end{pmatrix}$$

$$3 \times 3$$

$$= \begin{pmatrix} 9 & 2 & 2 \\ -2 & 0 & -1 \\ 6 & 4 & -2 \end{pmatrix}.$$

Given an $m \times n$ matrix $(a_{ij})$, the matrix products $(a_{ij}) \cdot (b_{ij})$ and $(b_{ij}) \cdot (a_{ij})$ are both defined if and only if $(b_{ij})$ is an $n \times m$ matrix. If this latter condition holds, so that it is possible to form both products, $(a_{ij}) \cdot (b_{ij})$ and $(b_{ij}) \cdot (a_{ij})$ will be of different sizes unless $m = n$.

Even if $m = n$, so that it makes sense to ask whether

$$(a_{ij}) \cdot (b_{ij}) = (b_{ij}) \cdot (a_{ij}),$$

matrix multiplication will not in general be commutative. This is seen by considering

$$\begin{pmatrix} 2 & 5 \\ 4 & 3 \end{pmatrix} \cdot \begin{pmatrix} 1 & 0 \\ -1 & 2 \end{pmatrix} = \begin{pmatrix} -3 & 10 \\ 1 & 6 \end{pmatrix} \neq \begin{pmatrix} 2 & 5 \\ 6 & 1 \end{pmatrix}$$

$$= \begin{pmatrix} 1 & 0 \\ -1 & 2 \end{pmatrix} \cdot \begin{pmatrix} 2 & 5 \\ 4 & 3 \end{pmatrix}.$$

It is quite possible, however, that a particular pair of matrices may commute.

For the zero matrices of appropriate dimensions, $(a_{ij}) \cdot 0 = 0$ and $0 \cdot (a_{ij}) = 0$. In particular, if both $(a_{ij})$ and $0$ are square matrices of the same order, then $(a_{ij}) \cdot 0 = 0 \cdot (a_{ij}) = 0$.

If $(a_{ij})$ is any square matrix, then that part of the matrix consisting of the elements $a_{ii}$ is called the *main diagonal* of the matrix.

**DEFINITION 4–9.** The *identity matrix of order n*, designated by $I_n$, or simply $I$ when there is no chance of confusion, is the square $n \times n$ matrix having ones down its main diagonal and zeros elsewhere.

It is helpful to have some notation for the elements of the identity matrix. Consequently, we will denote the element in the $i$th row and $j$th column of $I_n$ by the symbol $\delta_{ij}$, where

$$\delta_{ij} = \begin{cases} 1 & \text{for } i = j \\ 0 & \text{for } i \neq j \end{cases} \quad \text{(the Kronecker delta)},$$

and thus write $I_n = (\delta_{ij})$. For instance,

$$I_2 = \begin{pmatrix} \delta_{11} & \delta_{12} \\ \delta_{21} & \delta_{22} \end{pmatrix} = \begin{pmatrix} 1 & 0 \\ 0 & 1 \end{pmatrix}.$$

For each positive integer $n$, the set of square matrices of order $n$ will be represented by $M_n$ rather than $M_{n \times n}$. The identity matrix $I_n$ serves as an identity element for the operation of matrix multiplication in the set $M_n$. Indeed, if $(a_{ij}) \in M_n$, then

$$(a_{ij}) \cdot I_n = (a_{ij}) \cdot (\delta_{ij}) = \left( \sum_{k=1}^{n} a_{ik}\, \delta_{kj} \right) = (a_{ij}),$$

and similarly $I_n \cdot (a_{ij}) = (a_{ij})$.

We have just proved part of the following theorem:

**THEOREM 4-4.** The mathematical system $(M_n, +, \cdot)$ is a noncommutative ring with identity.

*Proof.* It has already been observed that $(M_n, +)$ is a commutative group and that matrix multiplication is a binary operation on $M_n$. What remains is to verify the associativity of multiplication and the distributive laws. To establish that multiplication is left distributive over addition, let $(a_{ij})$, $(b_{ij})$, and $(c_{ij}) \in M_n$. Then

$$(a_{ij}) \cdot [(b_{ij}) + (c_{ij})] = (a_{ij}) \cdot (b_{ij} + c_{ij})$$

$$= \left( \sum_{k=1}^{n} a_{ik}[b_{kj} + c_{kj}] \right)$$

$$= \left( \sum_{k=1}^{n} a_{ik}b_{kj} + \sum_{k=1}^{n} a_{ik}c_{kj} \right)$$

$$= \left( \sum_{k=1}^{n} a_{ik}b_{kj} \right) + \left( \sum_{k=1}^{n} a_{ik}c_{kj} \right)$$

$$= (a_{ij}) \cdot (b_{ij}) + (a_{ij}) \cdot (c_{ij}).$$

The rest of the proof offers no difficulty, and is omitted.

The ring $(M_n, +, \cdot)$ fails to satisfy the cancellation law. In particular, observe that while

$$\begin{pmatrix} 1 & 2 \\ 3 & 6 \end{pmatrix} \cdot \begin{pmatrix} 0 & 4 \\ 4 & 6 \end{pmatrix} = \begin{pmatrix} 8 & 16 \\ 24 & 48 \end{pmatrix} = \begin{pmatrix} 1 & 2 \\ 3 & 6 \end{pmatrix} \cdot \begin{pmatrix} 2 & 6 \\ 3 & 5 \end{pmatrix},$$

it is certainly not true that the matrices

$$\begin{pmatrix} 0 & 4 \\ 4 & 6 \end{pmatrix} \quad \text{and} \quad \begin{pmatrix} 2 & 6 \\ 3 & 5 \end{pmatrix}$$

are equal. We conclude then that the ring $(M_n, +, \cdot)$ must possess divisors of zero. This is obvious when we see that, for example,

$$\begin{pmatrix} 2 & 3 \\ 0 & 0 \end{pmatrix} \cdot \begin{pmatrix} 3 & 0 \\ -2 & 0 \end{pmatrix} = \begin{pmatrix} 0 & 0 \\ 0 & 0 \end{pmatrix}.$$

For our next theorem we need the following notation: Define $E_{ij}$ to be the $n \times n$ matrix having 1 as its $ij$th entry and zeros everywhere else. Thus for $n = 2$,

$$E_{11} = \begin{pmatrix} 1 & 0 \\ 0 & 0 \end{pmatrix}, \qquad E_{12} = \begin{pmatrix} 0 & 1 \\ 0 & 0 \end{pmatrix},$$

$$E_{21} = \begin{pmatrix} 0 & 0 \\ 1 & 0 \end{pmatrix}, \qquad E_{22} = \begin{pmatrix} 0 & 0 \\ 0 & 1 \end{pmatrix}.$$

Observe that, in general,

$$I_n = E_{11} + E_{22} + \cdots + E_{nn}$$

and

$$E_{ij} \cdot E_{st} = \begin{cases} E_{it} & \text{if } j = s, \\ 0 & \text{if } j \neq s. \end{cases}$$

It was pointed out in Problem 9, p. 83, that any commutative ring with identity which is not a field always possesses proper ideals. There is no reason to assume that in the absence of commutativity the same conclusion follows. Indeed, as we shall see, the system $(M_n, +, \cdot)$ provides an example of a noncommutative ring without proper ideals.

**THEOREM 4-5.** The ring of matrices $(M_n, +, \cdot)$ has no proper ideals.

*Proof.* Suppose that $(S, +, \cdot)$ is any ideal in $(M_n, +, \cdot)$, where $S \neq \{0\}$. Then $S$ must contain some nonzero matrix $(a_{ij})$, say, with $a_{st} \neq 0$. Now consider the matrix product

$$E_{ss} \cdot (b_{ij}) \cdot (a_{ij}) \cdot E_{tt},$$

where the matrix $(b_{ij})$ has the value $1/a_{st}$ down its main diagonal and zeros elsewhere. Due to the presence of all the zero entries in the various factors, this product is equal to $E_{st}$. Moreover, since $(S, +, \cdot)$ is an ideal, the matrix $E_{st}$ belongs to $S$. The relation

$$E_{ij} = E_{is} \cdot E_{st} \cdot E_{tj}, \qquad i, j = 1, 2, \ldots, n,$$

shows further that all $n^2$ of the matrices $E_{ij}$ are contained in $S$. The set $S$, being closed under addition, then has the identity matrix $I_n$ as a member, from which we conclude that $S = M_n$. In other words, if $S \neq \{0\}$, then $S = M_n$.

Matrices which have a multiplicative inverse are said to be *nonsingular;* otherwise they are called *singular.* Since a nonsingular matrix $(a_{ij})$ commutes with its inverse [by definition $(a_{ij}) \cdot (a_{ij})^{-1} = (a_{ij})^{-1} \cdot (a_{ij}) = I$], it follows that both the matrix and its inverse must be square and of the same order.

While only square matrices can possess an inverse, not every square matrix is nonsingular. For instance, consider the $2 \times 2$ matrix

$$\begin{pmatrix} 1 & 1 \\ 1 & 1 \end{pmatrix}.$$

If this matrix were nonsingular, we would then have

$$\begin{pmatrix} -1 & 1 \\ -1 & 1 \end{pmatrix} \cdot \left[ \begin{pmatrix} 1 & 1 \\ 1 & 1 \end{pmatrix} \cdot \begin{pmatrix} 1 & 1 \\ 1 & 1 \end{pmatrix}^{-1} \right] = \begin{pmatrix} -1 & 1 \\ -1 & 1 \end{pmatrix} \cdot I_2$$

$$= \begin{pmatrix} -1 & 1 \\ -1 & 1 \end{pmatrix}.$$

On the other hand, the associative law yields

$$\left[ \begin{pmatrix} -1 & 1 \\ -1 & 1 \end{pmatrix} \cdot \begin{pmatrix} 1 & 1 \\ 1 & 1 \end{pmatrix} \right] \cdot \begin{pmatrix} 1 & 1 \\ 1 & 1 \end{pmatrix}^{-1} = \begin{pmatrix} 0 & 0 \\ 0 & 0 \end{pmatrix} \cdot \begin{pmatrix} 1 & 1 \\ 1 & 1 \end{pmatrix}^{-1}$$

$$= \begin{pmatrix} 0 & 0 \\ 0 & 0 \end{pmatrix},$$

which leads to an obvious contradiction.

This argument shows that the system $(M_n - \{0\}, \cdot)$ does not constitute a group. However, by restricting our attention to those matrices which do have multiplicative inverses, we obtain the theorem:

**THEOREM 4–6.** If $M_n^*$ denotes the set of nonsingular matrices of order $n$, then the pair $(M_n^*, \cdot)$ is a noncommutative group.

By further limiting the set of matrices under consideration, we can obviously obtain more specialized results, as in the case of the next example.

EXAMPLE 4–3.    Consider the set $F$ of all $2 \times 2$ matrices of the form

$$\begin{pmatrix} a & b \\ -b & a \end{pmatrix}.$$

We will show that the system $(F, +, \cdot)$ is a field. If the matrices

$$\begin{pmatrix} a & b \\ -b & a \end{pmatrix} \quad \text{and} \quad \begin{pmatrix} c & d \\ -d & c \end{pmatrix}$$

are elements of the set $F$, then

$$\begin{pmatrix} a & b \\ -b & a \end{pmatrix} - \begin{pmatrix} c & d \\ -d & c \end{pmatrix} = \begin{pmatrix} a - c & b - d \\ -(b - d) & a - c \end{pmatrix},$$

$$\begin{pmatrix} a & b \\ -b & a \end{pmatrix} \cdot \begin{pmatrix} c & d \\ -d & c \end{pmatrix} = \begin{pmatrix} ac - bd & -(ad + bc) \\ ad + bc & ac - bd \end{pmatrix}.$$

Consequently, $F$ is closed under both differences and products. This makes $(F, +, \cdot)$ a subring of the ring of $2 \times 2$ matrices $(M_2, +, \cdot)$. It is readily verified that the elements of $F$ commute under matrix multiplication. Since the $2 \times 2$ identity matrix $I_2$ is clearly a member of $F$, $(F, +, \cdot)$ is a commutative ring with identity. All that remains is to show that each nonzero element of $F$ has a multiplicative inverse.

Now,

$$\begin{pmatrix} a & b \\ -b & a \end{pmatrix} = \begin{pmatrix} 0 & 0 \\ 0 & 0 \end{pmatrix}$$

if and only if $a = b = 0$. Thus, if $\begin{pmatrix} a & b \\ -b & a \end{pmatrix} \neq 0$, then $a^2 + b^2 \neq 0$ and

$$\begin{pmatrix} a & b \\ -b & a \end{pmatrix}^{-1} = \begin{pmatrix} \dfrac{a}{a^2 + b^2} & \dfrac{b}{a^2 + b^2} \\ -\dfrac{b}{a^2 + b^2} & \dfrac{a}{a^2 + b^2} \end{pmatrix} \in F,$$

as a direct computation will establish.

It is interesting to note that the additive groups $(F, +)$ and $(V_2, +)$ are algebraically equivalent under the mapping $\phi \colon F \to V_2$ defined by

$$\phi \left[ \begin{pmatrix} a & b \\ -b & a \end{pmatrix} \right] = (a, b).$$

This function is plainly operation-preserving, for

$$\phi\left[\begin{pmatrix} a & b \\ -b & a \end{pmatrix} + \begin{pmatrix} c & d \\ -d & c \end{pmatrix}\right] = \phi\left[\begin{pmatrix} a+c & b+d \\ -(b+d) & c+d \end{pmatrix}\right]$$

$$= (a+c, b+d)$$

$$= (a, b) + (c, d)$$

$$= \phi\left[\begin{pmatrix} a & b \\ -b & a \end{pmatrix}\right] + \phi\left[\begin{pmatrix} c & d \\ -d & c \end{pmatrix}\right].$$

If

$$\phi\left[\begin{pmatrix} a & b \\ -b & a \end{pmatrix}\right] = \phi\left[\begin{pmatrix} c & d \\ -d & c \end{pmatrix}\right],$$

then from the definition of equality of the vectors $(a, b)$ and $(c, d)$, we have $a = c, b = d$. This means that

$$\begin{pmatrix} a & b \\ -b & a \end{pmatrix} = \begin{pmatrix} c & d \\ -d & c \end{pmatrix},$$

so that $\phi$ is a one-to-one mapping. It is clearly onto $V_2$.

A stronger result, which we shall leave as an exercise, is that the field $(F, +, \cdot)$ is algebraically equivalent to the complex numbers $(C, +, \cdot)$ under the function

$$\Phi\left[\begin{pmatrix} a & b \\ -b & a \end{pmatrix}\right] = a + bi.$$

Before concluding this section let us briefly consider a technique for finding the inverse of a square matrix, if such an inverse exists. The so-called "elementary row operations" on matrices are:

(1) multiplying a row by a fixed nonzero constant;

(2) interchanging any two rows;

(3) adding a multiple of one row to another row.

If $A = (a_{ij})$ is any square matrix of order $n$, append to it the identity matrix $I_n$, thus forming an $n \times 2n$ block matrix $(A \mid I_n)$. The vertical line is used here to enable us to distinguish at a glance the original matrix from the appended identity. Now, perform a sequence of elementary row operations on this enlarged matrix with the purpose of transforming $A$ into the identity matrix, if possible. At each stage, the necessary elementary row operation is applied to the matrix obtained from the preceding row operation. When $A$ is nonsingular, the final matrix takes the form

$(I_n \mid B)$, where $B = A^{-1}$. If $A$ cannot be so reduced to the identity matrix, then it fails to have an inverse.

It will be helpful to illustrate this procedure with an example.

EXAMPLE 4–4. To calculate the inverse of the matrix

$$A = \begin{pmatrix} -1 & 0 & 2 \\ 0 & 1 & 0 \\ 2 & 1 & -3 \end{pmatrix},$$

we perform a sequence of row operations on the $3 \times 6$ matrix $(A \mid I_3)$ designed to yield $(I_3 \mid B)$. One such sequence is the following:

$$\begin{pmatrix} -1 & 0 & 2 & 1 & 0 & 0 \\ 0 & 1 & 0 & 0 & 1 & 0 \\ 2 & 1 & -3 & 0 & 0 & 1 \end{pmatrix}$$

$$\xrightarrow{-R_1} \begin{pmatrix} 1 & 0 & -2 & -1 & 0 & 0 \\ 0 & 1 & 0 & 0 & 1 & 0 \\ 2 & 1 & -3 & 0 & 0 & 1 \end{pmatrix}$$

$$\xrightarrow{R_3 - 2R_1} \begin{pmatrix} 1 & 0 & -2 & -1 & 0 & 0 \\ 0 & 1 & 0 & 0 & 1 & 0 \\ 0 & 0 & 1 & 2 & 0 & 1 \end{pmatrix}$$

$$\xrightarrow{R_1 + 2R_3} \begin{pmatrix} 1 & 0 & 0 & 3 & 0 & 2 \\ 0 & 1 & 0 & 0 & 1 & 0 \\ 0 & 0 & 1 & 2 & 0 & 1 \end{pmatrix}$$

Thus

$$A^{-1} = \begin{pmatrix} 3 & 0 & 2 \\ 0 & 1 & 0 \\ 2 & 0 & 1 \end{pmatrix}.$$

One of the principal applications of matrix theory is in the solution of systems of linear equations. Let us consider a system

$$\begin{aligned} a_{11}x_1 + a_{12}x_2 + \cdots + a_{1n}x_n &= b_1, \\ a_{21}x_1 + a_{22}x_2 + \cdots + a_{2n}x_n &= b_2, \\ &\vdots \\ a_{n1}x_1 + a_{n2}x_2 + \cdots + a_{nn}x_n &= b_n, \end{aligned}$$

where the coefficients $a_{ij}$ and the $b_i$ are real numbers. We seek a set of values $x_1, x_2, \ldots, x_n$ which simultaneously satisfy these $n$ equations.

This system can conveniently be written as a single matrix equation

$$\begin{pmatrix} a_{11} & a_{12} & \cdots & a_{1n} \\ a_{21} & a_{22} & \cdots & a_{2n} \\ \vdots & \vdots & & \vdots \\ a_{n1} & a_{n2} & \cdots & a_{nn} \end{pmatrix} \cdot \begin{pmatrix} x_1 \\ x_2 \\ \vdots \\ x_n \end{pmatrix} = \begin{pmatrix} b_1 \\ b_2 \\ \vdots \\ b_n \end{pmatrix},$$

or more concisely as

$$(a_{ij}) \cdot (x_i) = (b_i).$$

If the matrix of coefficients $(a_{ij})$ is nonsingular, then multiplying both sides of the equation $(a_{ij}) \cdot (x_i) = (b_i)$ by its inverse, we obtain

$$(x_i) = (a_{ij})^{-1} \cdot (b_i),$$

from which we can read off the value of the unknowns $x_i$.

## PROBLEMS

1. Determine the values of $a$ and $b$ for which the following matrix equation holds:

$$\begin{pmatrix} 3 & 0 \\ 1 & 1 \\ 5 & 2 \end{pmatrix} \cdot \begin{pmatrix} 4 & 7 \\ 6 & 8 \end{pmatrix} + 2 \begin{pmatrix} a & -3 \\ 0 & 5 \\ 4 & b \end{pmatrix} = \begin{pmatrix} 20 & 15 \\ 10 & 25 \\ 40 & 25 \end{pmatrix}.$$

2. Compute $A \cdot B$, $A^2$, $B \cdot C$, $C \cdot A$, and $C \cdot B$ for the matrices

$$A = \begin{pmatrix} 0 & 1 & -1 \\ 0 & 0 & 1 \\ 1 & 0 & -1 \end{pmatrix}, \quad B = \begin{pmatrix} 1 & 2 \\ 3 & 4 \\ 5 & 6 \end{pmatrix}, \quad C = \begin{pmatrix} 3 & 0 & -1 \\ 4 & -5 & 1 \end{pmatrix}.$$

3. Show that each of the matrices

$$\begin{pmatrix} 1 & 0 \\ 0 & 1 \end{pmatrix}, \quad \begin{pmatrix} 4 & 0 \\ 0 & 4 \end{pmatrix} \quad \text{and} \quad \begin{pmatrix} 3 & -2 \\ -1 & 2 \end{pmatrix}$$

is a solution of the matrix equation $X^2 - 5X + 4I = 0$.

4. (a) Find a matrix whose square is the matrix

$$\begin{pmatrix} 3 & -4 \\ 1 & -1 \end{pmatrix}.$$

(b) Obtain all matrices that commute with

$$\begin{pmatrix} 1 & 2 \\ 0 & 2 \end{pmatrix}.$$

5. Prove that

$$\begin{pmatrix} 0 & a & b \\ 0 & 0 & c \\ 0 & 0 & 0 \end{pmatrix}^3 = 0.$$

State an analogous result for $n \times n$ matrices.

6. (a) Let the set $G$ consist of all matrices of the form

$$\begin{pmatrix} a & b \\ 0 & 1 \end{pmatrix}$$

with $a \neq 0$. Prove that the system $(G, \cdot)$ is a group, where $\cdot$ denotes the usual matrix multiplication.

(b) If $H$ denotes the set of matrices of the type

$$\begin{pmatrix} 1 & c \\ 0 & 1 \end{pmatrix},$$

show that $(H, \cdot)$ is a normal subgroup of $(G, \cdot)$.

7. Find the center of the ring $(M_2, +, \cdot)$.

8. Given that the set $F$ denotes the collection of all matrices of the form

$$\begin{pmatrix} a & 3b \\ b & a \end{pmatrix},$$

prove that $(F, +, \cdot)$ is a field.

9. (a) Determine a necessary and sufficient condition on the elements $a, b, c, d,$ so that the matrix

$$\begin{pmatrix} a & b \\ c & d \end{pmatrix}$$

is nonsingular.

(b) Obtain the inverses of the following nonsingular matrices:

$$\begin{pmatrix} 1 & 2 \\ 1 & -1 \end{pmatrix},$$

$$\begin{pmatrix} 2 & 1 & 0 \\ 1 & 2 & 1 \\ -1 & 0 & 3 \end{pmatrix}, \quad \begin{pmatrix} 3 & -1 & -1 \\ 2 & 1 & 4 \\ 4 & 3 & 5 \end{pmatrix}.$$

10. Suppose that the set $R$ consists of all $2 \times 2$ matrices of the form

$$\begin{pmatrix} a & b \\ 0 & c \end{pmatrix}.$$

(a) Establish that $(R, +, \cdot)$ is a subring of the ring $(M_2, +, \cdot)$.

(b) Given that $S$ consists of matrices of the type

$$\begin{pmatrix} 0 & b \\ 0 & 0 \end{pmatrix},$$

determine whether the system $(S, +, \cdot)$ is an ideal in $(R, +, \cdot)$.

11. Using Example 4–3, show that the field $(F, +, \cdot)$ is algebraically equivalent to the complex numbers under the mapping

$$f\left[\begin{pmatrix} a & b \\ -b & a \end{pmatrix}\right] = a + bi.$$

12. Let the set $G$ be comprised of the following matrices:

$$I = \begin{pmatrix} 1 & 0 \\ 0 & 1 \end{pmatrix}, \qquad S = \begin{pmatrix} 0 & 1 \\ -1 & 0 \end{pmatrix}, \qquad T = \begin{pmatrix} -1 & 0 \\ 0 & -1 \end{pmatrix},$$

$$U = \begin{pmatrix} 0 & -1 \\ 1 & 0 \end{pmatrix}, \qquad V = \begin{pmatrix} 1 & 0 \\ 0 & -1 \end{pmatrix}, \qquad W = \begin{pmatrix} 0 & 1 \\ 1 & 0 \end{pmatrix},$$

$$X = \begin{pmatrix} -1 & 0 \\ 0 & 1 \end{pmatrix}, \qquad Y = \begin{pmatrix} 0 & -1 \\ -1 & 0 \end{pmatrix}.$$

(a) Prove that $(G, \cdot)$ is a group.
(b) If $H = \{I, S, T, U\}$, show that $(H, \cdot)$ is a normal subgroup of $(G, \cdot)$.
(c) Find the distinct cosets of $H$ in $G$.

13. Let $M$ be the set of all $3 \times 3$ matrices having elements 0 and 1 in such a way that there is exactly one 1 in each row and column. Prove that $(M, \cdot)$ is a group.

## 4–2.   VECTOR SPACES

We saw in the last section that the collection $M_n$ of square matrices of order $n$, together with the operations of matrix addition and multiplication, constitutes a ring. At the time, our third matrix operation, the multiplication of a matrix by a real number, seemed relatively unimportant, especially since it failed to be even a binary operation on $M_n$.

However, by abstracting the essential features of this operation, we can define a mathematical system having the set $M_n$ (more generally, the set $M_{m \times n}$) under matrix addition and multiplication by the reals as a model. Basically, this will be a matter of combining two different algebraic systems into a single system known as a vector space.

As the reader should expect by now, a formal investigation of vector spaces involves the consideration of such notions as subsystems, operation-preserving functions, algebraic equivalence, etc. We shall briefly touch on these concepts here in order to indicate their appropriate analogues. Our main objective, however, is to place the study of matrices in a more general algebraic context rather than to develop an extensive theory of vector spaces.

> **DEFINITION 4–10.** A *vector space* (or *linear space*) *over the field F* consists of the following:
>
> (1) a commutative group $(V, +)$ whose elements are called *vectors;*
> (2) a field $(F, +, \cdot)$ whose elements are called *scalars;*
> (3) an operation $\circ$ of *scalar multiplication* connecting the group and field which satisfies the properties:
>
>> (a) for each $c \in F$ and $x \in V$, there is defined an element $c \circ x \in V$; that is, $V$ is closed under left multiplication by scalars;
>> (b) $(c_1 + c_2) \circ x = (c_1 \circ x) + (c_2 \circ x)$;
>> (c) $(c_1 \circ c_2) \circ x = c_1 \circ (c_2 \circ x)$,
>> (d) $c \circ (x + y) = (c \circ x) + (c \circ y)$;
>> (e) $1 \circ x = x$, where 1 is the field identity element.

A vector space over the field $F$ shall be denoted merely by $V(F)$, rather than by the more precise but cumbersome notation

$$((V, +), (F, +, \cdot), \circ).$$

For further simplicity we shall write $cx$ for $c \circ x$.

While the addition symbol has been used in two different contexts in Definition 4–10, to designate the operation of the group and one of the operations of the field, there should be no confusion. It will always be clear in a given situation whether vectors or scalars are being added. When both vector addition and scalar multiplication are involved in an expression, we follow our usual convention in omitting parentheses.

Observe that the hypothesis $1x = x$ is quite essential. For without it, every field and commutative group would become a vector space under the trivial scalar multiplication whereby $cx = 0$ for all $c \in F$, $x \in V$.

In the following selection of examples of vector spaces, we shall always take the underlying field of scalars as being $(R^{\#}, +, \cdot)$.

EXAMPLE 4–5. Let the commutative group be $(M_{m \times n}, +)$, where $M_{m \times n}$ is the set of all $m \times n$ matrices and $+$ is the operation of matrix addition.

For $c \in R^\#$ and $(a_{ij}) \in M_{m \times n}$, define scalar multiplication by

$$c(a_{ij}) = (ca_{ij}) \in M_{m \times n}.$$

The results of the previous section show that we thus obtain a vector space. We will denote the particular vector space which arises when $m = n$ by $M_n(R^\#)$.

EXAMPLE 4–6. If $V_n$ denotes the collection of $n$-component row vectors and $+$ the usual componentwise addition of vectors, then $(V, +)$ is a commutative group. A vector space results on defining scalar multiplication by

$$c(x_k) = (cx_k) \in V_n \qquad \text{for} \qquad c \in R^\#, \quad (x_k) \in V_n.$$

This vector space will subsequently be represented by $V_n(R^\#)$.

EXAMPLE 4–7. Let $V$ be the set of all real-valued functions having the closed interval $[a, b]$ as their domain, with pointwise addition as the group operation. For $c \in R^\#$ and $f \in V$, scalar multiplication is defined by specifying the functional value of $cf$ at each point in $[a, b]$:

$$(cf)(x) = cf(x) \qquad \text{for} \qquad x \in [a, b].$$

EXAMPLE 4–8. Suppose $P$ is the set of all polynomials in a variable $x$ with real coefficients. Then $(P, +)$ is a commutative group. For $c \in R^\#$ and $p \in P$, a vector space is obtained by requiring that

$$(cp)(x) = cp(x).$$

The symbol 0 shall be used to designate both the zero elements of $V$ and $F$. The additive inverse of a scalar $c \in F$ is denoted by $-c$, while the inverse of a vector $x \in V$ is also represented by $-x$. These ambiguities should not lead to any confusion if the reader attends closely to the context in which the notation is employed. Some simple consequences of Definition 4–10 are embodied in the next theorem.

**THEOREM 4–7.** For any $c \in F$ and $x \in V$,

(1) $0x = 0$;

(2) $c0 = 0$;

(3) $-(cx) = (-c)x = c(-x)$.

*Proof.* To establish (1), we use the field result $0 + 1 = 1$. Then

$$0x + x = 0x + 1x = (0 + 1)x = 1x = x = 0 + x.$$

Since $(V, +)$ is a group, the cancellation yields $0x = 0$.

The proof of the second part of the theorem follows from the group result $0 + x = x$. We have

$$c0 + cx = c(0 + x) = cx = 0 + cx.$$

Again the cancellation law gives the desired conclusion.

Finally, to obtain (3), observe that

$$0 = 0x = [c + (-c)]x = cx + (-c)x.$$

This means that

$$(-c)x = -(cx).$$

Similarly,

$$0 = c0 = c[x + (-x)] = cx + c(-x)$$

which proves $c(-x) = -(cx)$.

Whenever a mathematical system has been considered, the question of subsystems arose. In the case of vector spaces, the sub-vector spaces are referred to as subspaces.

> **DEFINITION 4–11.** Let $V(F)$ be a vector space over the field $F$ and $W \subseteq V$, with $W \neq \emptyset$. Then $W(F)$ is a *subspace* of $V(F)$ provided that $W(F)$ satisfies the vector space axioms when equipped with the same operations defined on $V(F)$.

Since $W \subseteq V$, much of the algebraic structure of $W(F)$ is inherited from $V(F)$. The minimum conditions that $W(F)$ must satisfy to be a subspace are:

(1) $(W, +)$ is a subgroup of $(V, +)$;

(2) $W$ is closed under scalar multiplication.

The usual criterion for deciding whether $(W, +)$ is a subgroup of $(V, +)$ is to see if $W$ is closed under differences. The second of the above conditions implies that $-x = (-1)x$ will belong to $W$ whenever $x$ is an element of $W$. Because $x - y = x + (-y)$, condition (2), together with the closure of $W$ under addition, is sufficient to guarantee that $W$ be closed under differences. This observation allows us to reformulate Definition 4–11 as follows:

> **DEFINITION 4–12.** $W(F)$ is a subspace of the vector space $V(F)$ if $W$ is a nonempty subset of $V$ such that
>
> (1) $x, y \in W$ implies $x + y \in W$;
>
> (2) $x \in W$ and $c \in F$ imply $cx \in W$.

EXAMPLE 4–9. Consider the set $W$ of vectors in $V_3(R^\#)$ whose components add up to zero:

$$W = \{(x_1, x_2, x_3) \mid x_1 + x_2 + x_3 = 0\}.$$

If $(x_1, x_2, x_3)$ and $(y_1, y_2, y_3)$ are arbitrary elements of $W$, then their sum $(x_1 + y_1, x_2 + y_2, x_3 + y_3)$ is such that

$$(x_1 + y_1) + (x_2 + y_2) + (x_3 + y_3)$$
$$= (x_1 + x_2 + x_3) + (y_1 + y_2 + y_3)$$
$$= 0 + 0$$
$$= 0.$$

This shows the closure of $W$ under addition. It is equally clear that $W$ is also closed under scalar multiplication. Consequently, $W(R^\#)$ is a subspace of $V_3(R^\#)$.

EXAMPLE 4–10. Let $W$ denote the collection of all elements of $M_2(R^\#)$ of the form

$$\begin{pmatrix} a & b \\ -b & a \end{pmatrix}.$$

It follows immediately from the definition of the matrix operations in $M_2(R^\#)$ that $W(R^\#)$ is a subspace, for

$$\begin{pmatrix} a & b \\ -b & a \end{pmatrix} + \begin{pmatrix} c & d \\ -d & c \end{pmatrix} = \begin{pmatrix} a + c & b + d \\ -(b + d) & a + c \end{pmatrix} \in W,$$

$$k \begin{pmatrix} a & b \\ -b & a \end{pmatrix} = \begin{pmatrix} ka & kb \\ -(kb) & ka \end{pmatrix} \in W.$$

From our study of other subsystems, we should expect the intersection of subspaces also to be a subspace, and indeed this is stated in the next theorem.

**THEOREM 4–8.** If $W_1(F)$ and $W_2(F)$ are subspaces of the vector space $V(F)$, then so also is $(W_1 \cap W_2)(F)$.

*Proof.* The set $W_1 \cap W_2$ is not empty, for it at least contains $0$. Suppose $x$ and $y$ are arbitrary vectors in $W_1 \cap W_2$ and $c \in F$. Then since both $W_1(F)$ and $W_2(F)$ are subspaces, $x + y \in W_1$, $cx \in W_1$, and $x + y \in W_2$, $cx \in W_2$. That is, $x + y \in W_1 \cap W_2$, $cx \in W_1 \cap W_2$. Thus $(W_1 \cap W_2)(F)$ is a subspace of $V(F)$, since $W_1 \cap W_2$ is closed under its operations.

**DEFINITION 4–13.** If $V(F)$ and $V'(F)$ are vector spaces over the same field, then the mapping $f \colon V \to V'$ is said to be *operation-preserving* if

$$f(x + y) = f(x) + f(y),$$
$$f(cx) = cf(x),$$

for every pair of elements $x, y \in V$ and $c \in F$. That is, $f$ preserves both vector addition and scalar multiplication.

As usual, the vector spaces $V(F)$ and $V'(F)$ are *algebraically equivalent* whenever there exists a one-to-one operation-preserving function from $V$ onto $V'$.

EXAMPLE 4–11. As was seen in Example 4–10, if

$$W = \left\{ \begin{pmatrix} a & b \\ -b & a \end{pmatrix} \middle| \, a, b \in R^{\#} \right\},$$

then $W(R^{\#})$ is a vector subspace of $M_2(R^{\#})$; that is, $W(R^{\#})$ is itself a vector space under the operations of matrix addition and multiplication by real numbers. We will now show that $W(R^{\#})$ is algebraically equivalent to the vector space $V_2(R^{\#})$ under the mapping $f \colon W \to V_2$ defined by

$$f\left[ \begin{pmatrix} a & b \\ -b & a \end{pmatrix} \right] = (a, b).$$

It has previously been established (recall Example 4–3) that the function $f$ preserves sums and is a one-to-one onto mapping. Consequently, all that remains is to prove that $f$ preserves scalar products. This is readily verified, for

$$f\left[ c \begin{pmatrix} a & b \\ -b & a \end{pmatrix} \right] = f\left[ \begin{pmatrix} ca & cb \\ -cb & ca \end{pmatrix} \right]$$
$$= (ca, cb)$$
$$= c(a, b)$$
$$= cf\left[ \begin{pmatrix} a & b \\ -b & a \end{pmatrix} \right].$$

A vector space $V(F)$ is said to be an *algebra over the field* $F$ if its elements can be multiplied in such a way that $V(F)$ is also a ring in which scalar multiplication is related to ring multiplication by the following *mixed associative law:*

$$c(xy) = (cx)y = x(cy) \qquad (x, y \in V; c \in F).$$

Obvious examples of rings which are also algebras are the ring of matrices of order $n$, the ring of real-valued functions with the interval $[a, b]$ as the domain, as well as both the real and complex number fields.

Since an algebra is simultaneously a ring and a vector space, any operation-preserving function between algebras must preserve both the ring and the vector space operations. That is, an operation-preserving function $f$ between two algebras over the same field is such that:

$$f(x + y) = f(x) + f(y),$$
$$f(xy) = f(x)f(y),$$
$$f(cx) = cf(x).$$

We shall conclude our study of mathematical systems with the following interesting example.

EXAMPLE 4-12. Let the set $V$ consist of all $2 \times 2$ matrices of the form

$$\begin{pmatrix} a & b \\ 0 & c \end{pmatrix}.$$

Then $(V, +, \cdot)$ is a noncommutative ring with identity (Problem 10, p. 106), as well as a vector space over the real numbers (Problem 7, p. 115). In fact, the system $(V, +, \cdot)$ is an algebra. Our purpose here is to determine the nature of the operation-preserving functions from this algebra into the real numbers. On setting

$$I = \begin{pmatrix} 1 & 0 \\ 0 & 1 \end{pmatrix}, \qquad X = \begin{pmatrix} 0 & 1 \\ 0 & 0 \end{pmatrix}, \qquad Y = \begin{pmatrix} 0 & 0 \\ 0 & 1 \end{pmatrix},$$

we may represent each element of $V$ by

$$\begin{pmatrix} a & b \\ 0 & c \end{pmatrix} = aI + bX + (c - a)Y.$$

Thus, if $f$ is any operation-preserving function from the algebra $(V, +, \cdot)$ into the algebra $(R^{\#}, +, \cdot)$, then

$$f\left[ \begin{pmatrix} a & b \\ 0 & c \end{pmatrix} \right] = af(I) + bf(X) + (c - a)f(Y).$$

As usual, multiplicative identities must map into each other, so that $f(I) = 1$. Since the matrix $X$ happens to be nilpotent (in particular, $X^2 = 0$), it follows from Problem 15 (p. 83) that $f(X) = 0$. Observe also that the matrix $Y$ is idempotent; that is, $Y^2 = Y$. This implies that $f(Y)$ must assume either the value zero or one.

From this discussion, we conclude that

$$f\left[\begin{pmatrix} a & b \\ 0 & c \end{pmatrix}\right] = a \quad \text{or} \quad f\left[\begin{pmatrix} a & b \\ 0 & c \end{pmatrix}\right] = c.$$

Defining

$$f_1\left[\begin{pmatrix} a & b \\ 0 & c \end{pmatrix}\right] = a \quad \text{and} \quad f_2\left[\begin{pmatrix} a & b \\ 0 & c \end{pmatrix}\right] = c,$$

it follows that $f_1$ and $f_2$ are actually operation-preserving functions from $(V, +, \cdot)$ to the real numbers. Our argument shows these to be the only functions with this property.

## PROBLEMS

1. Prove that in any vector space $V(F)$, if $x, y \in V$ and $c \in F$, then
   (a) $c(x - y) = cx - cy$,
   (b) $cx = 0$ implies either $c = 0$ or $x = 0$.

2. Let $V$ be the set of all ordered pairs of real numbers. Define an operation $+$ in $V$ by the rule

   $$(x_1, y_1) + (x_2, y_2) = (3(y_1 + y_2), -(x_1 + x_2)).$$

   Furthermore, define scalar multiplication in $V$ by

   $$c(x, y) = (3cy, -cx), \quad c \in R^{\#}.$$

   Determine whether $V(R^{\#})$ is a vector space.

3. In any vector space $V(F)$, show that the following cancellation laws hold:
   (a) If $x \in V$ with $x \neq 0$, then $c_1 x = c_2 x$ implies $c_1 = c_2$.
   (b) If $x, y$ are nonzero elements of $V$, then $cx = cy$ with $c \neq 0$ implies $x = y$.

4. For each of the following sets $W$, determine whether $W(R^{\#})$ is a subspace of the vector space $V_n(R^{\#})$:
   (a) $W$ consists of all vectors $(x_1, x_2, \ldots, x_n)$ such that $x_n = 0$.
   (b) $W$ consists of all vectors $(x_1, x_2, \ldots, x_n)$ such that $x_1 = 1$.
   (c) $W$ consists of all vectors $(x_1, x_2, \ldots, x_n)$ such that $x_1 = x_2 = \cdots = x_n$.

5. If $W_1(F)$ and $W_2(F)$ are subspaces of the vector space $V(F)$, define

   $$W_1 + W_2 = \{x + y \mid x \in W_1, y \in W_2\}.$$

   (a) Show that $(W_1 + W_2)(F)$ is a subspace of $V(F)$.
   (b) Prove that a vector $w \in W_1 + W_2$ is uniquely expressible as $w = x + y$ with $x \in W, y \in W_2$, if and only if $W_1 \cap W_2 = \{0\}$.

6. Let $V(R^\#)$ be the vector space of real-valued functions on the interval $[a, b]$ under pointwise addition and multiplication by a real number.

   (a) If $W$ is the set of all functions $f$ in $V$ such that $f(a) = 0$, is $W(R^\#)$ a subspace of $V(R^\#)$?

   (b) If $W$ is the set of all functions $f$ in $V$ for which $f(a) = f(b)$, is $W(R^\#)$ a subspace of $V(R^\#)$?

7. Show that for the following sets $W$ of matrices, $W(R^\#)$ is a subspace of $M_2(R^\#)$:

   (a) all matrices of the form

   $$\begin{pmatrix} a & b \\ 0 & c \end{pmatrix};$$

   (b) all matrices of the form

   $$\begin{pmatrix} a & 0 \\ 0 & a \end{pmatrix}.$$

8. Prove that $V_2(R^\#)$ is algebraically equivalent to itself under the mapping $f[(a, b)] = (b, a)$.

9. Suppose $f$ is an operation-preserving function from the vector space $V(F)$ into the vector space $V'(F)$.

   (a) Show that $f(0) = 0$.

   (b) Given that $\ker(f) = \{x \in V \mid f(x) = 0\}$, prove that $(\ker(f))(F)$ is a subspace of $V(F)$.

# NOTATION INDEX

# INDEX